PEN&INK
DRAWING
WORKBOOK

PEN&INK
DRAWING
WORKBOOK

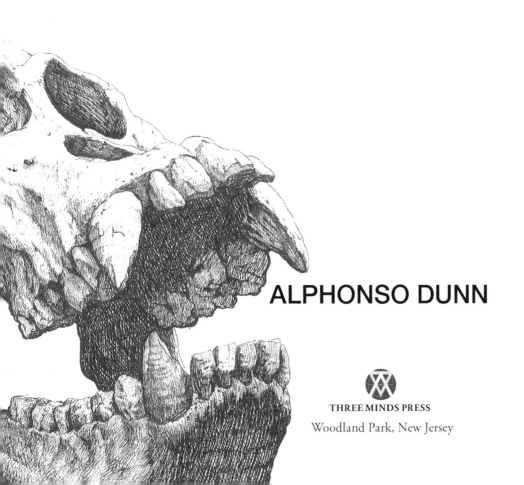

ALPHONSO DUNN

THREE MINDS PRESS

Woodland Park, New Jersey

ABOUT THE AUTHOR

Alphonso Dunn is a consummate draftsman, illustrator, high school chemistry teacher, and college instructor. He is a graduate of the New York Academy of Art and an award-winning artist. Alphonso's work can be found in several private collections in the US and worldwide. Currently, he is working on new book projects, creating new work, and sharing art instruction with his over 400,000 followers on YouTube. With hundreds of free tutorials on drawing, pen and ink, watercolor, urban sketching, and more, Alphonso Dunn's YouTube channel has become a trusted destination for quality art instruction. Join him on YouTube, Facebook, and Instagram @alphonsodunn

Senior Editor: Loraine Laidlaw
Associate Editor: Kisha Edwards-Gandsy
Cover Design: Bob Fillie

Published in 2018 by Three Minds Press
Woodland Park, New Jersey

Library of Congress Control Cataloging-in-Publication Data`
Dunn, Alphonso.
    Pen and Ink Drawing Workbook/Alphonso Dunn
    1. Pen drawing—Technique.   I. Title.
    ISBN 0-9970-4650-3

First Edition. First paperback printing, 2018

Manufactured in the United States of America.

To my family, friends, and virtual students all over the world

Contents

Introduction

Why this Workbook?

This is the official workbook for *Pen and Ink Drawing: A Simple Guide*. Its purpose is to provide you with the exercises you need to develop and refine your pen and ink drawing skills and techniques. As you toil through the pages of this workbook, take the liberty to refer back to the complementary text to refresh, review, or clarify concepts as often as you need to. They were written to work best hand in hand.

This book is one of the first of its kind; an actual drawing workbook that is loaded with over 100 engaging drills and exercises that cover a wide range of skills, techniques, and concepts, essential to learning the wonderful art of pen and ink drawing.

There is an impressive array of drills and exercises that will keep you engaged and inspired from cover to cover. Many of these exercises will have sample drawings, which will demonstrate the concepts, skills, or techniques you will practice. These are meant to inspire you and can be used as models to copy and study. This workbook provides ample space to draw and occasionally includes a copy of a demo drawing that you can trace. Tracing a demo drawing provides a unique learning experience, which allows you to simulate the process used to create the drawing, and helps you to prepare for drawing independently.

In addition, some exercises provide a faint outline of the demo drawing. This is like having a pencil under-drawing done for you, which saves you time, provides convenience, and allows you to focus fully on your ink work. Nonetheless, you may still feel the need to pencil in a few cross-contour lines, sketch in some details, or make other notations as guides or reminders.

This book is all about you. It was inspired by you, started for you, and will be completed by you. Invest yourself in every exercise and allow yourself to progress through the content steadily. Do not rush. Take breaks if needed and make time to reflect. Remember that drawing is as much a mental activity as it is a mechanical one.

My goals for this book:

I hope that after completing this book, you will:

- Learn invaluable concepts, skills, and techniques that will significantly improve your proficiency with pen and ink.
- Appreciate the uniqueness, versatility, and expressive power of this wonderful art form.
- Use all you learn to further enrich your life.

How to get the most from this workbook?

Remember, this is a "work"book and to get the most from it, you must:

- Be patient. Some things just cannot be rushed. Learning to draw with ink is one of them.
- Be willing to practice the same thing over and over again. Repetition is the mother of learning.
- Understand that learning isn't always fun. Some drills may feel boring, but just do them. Your work will pay off eventually.
- Be persistent. Don't give up after your 1st, 2nd, 3rd, 4th… or 100th attempt. Celebrate the small steps of your journey and keep going.
- Do not rush your drawing or your strokes. Pen and ink can be unforgiving.
- Be positive. Having the right attitude is half the job. Don't be too hard on yourself or be quick to compare yourself to others. Compete with you.
- Believe in yourself. Know what you're capable of and let no one tell you otherwise.

Supplies:

These are the recommended materials for completing the exercises of this workbook:

- Fine-point drawing pen (about 0.20mm or smaller).
- Medium-point drawing pen (about 0.30mm).
- Ink drawing instrument that can vary line weight (brush pen, fountain pen, dip pen, etc.).
- White ink pen.
- HB pencil (not too hard and not too soft).
- Eraser (plastic or kneaded).
- Paper (archival, acid-free, medium-weight, and smooth).

If all you have is a simple ballpoint pen, then that will suffice. Learning the key principles and drawing process is what matters most.

NOTES

Strokes

The exercises of this section are based primarily on the content of chapters two and three of *Pen & Ink Drawing: A Simple Guide*. Your success in pen and ink drawing will most likely be based on your proficiency in handling the basic strokes: it all starts there. Take your time to develop consistency and stable pen control, and learn to comfortably manipulate all the variations of a stroke. These will form the foundation of your practice. Line quality is heavily influenced by how well you handle the drawing instrument. And virtually all visual effects originate in some way from the use of the five stroke variations. So, most of the drills and exercises in this section are designed to focus your efforts specifically on these key elements.

MAKING STROKES CONSISTENT

There are four keys to maintaining consistency in your strokes: spacing, size, weight, and direction. Your strokes need not be perfect or identical but should be uniformed enough to convincingly convey cohesion. To develop consistency, do not rush your strokes. Focus on drawing at a steady, controlled pace.

Spacing

Size

Weight

Direction

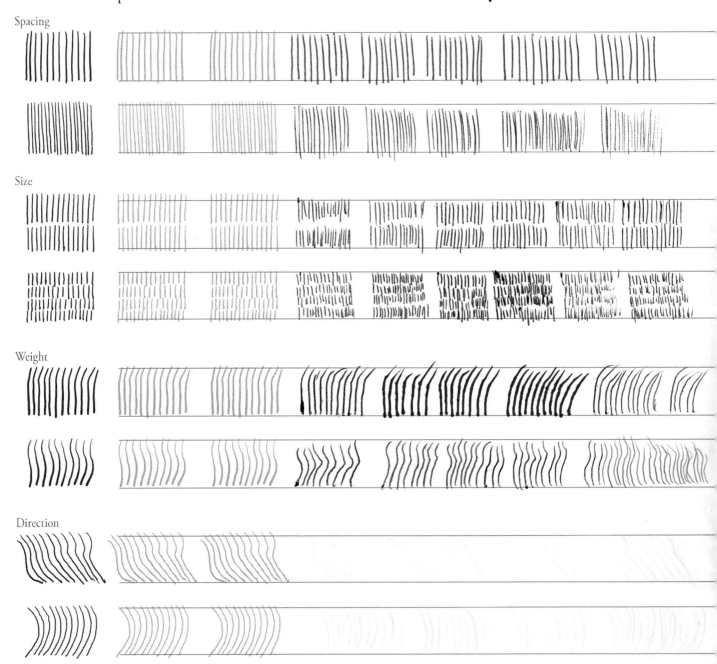

-06.21.2024-

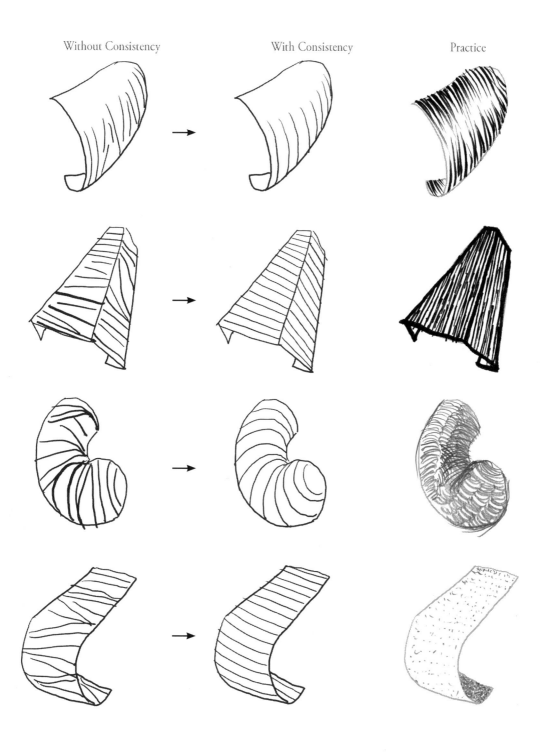

Without Consistency   With Consistency   Practice

STRAIGHT LINES

To improve your pen control, think about how far up the shaft you hold the instrument, how tight is your grip, and how hard you are pressing down. Use a moderate grip, and allow the base of your hand to help anchor and stabilize your movement.

06.21.2024

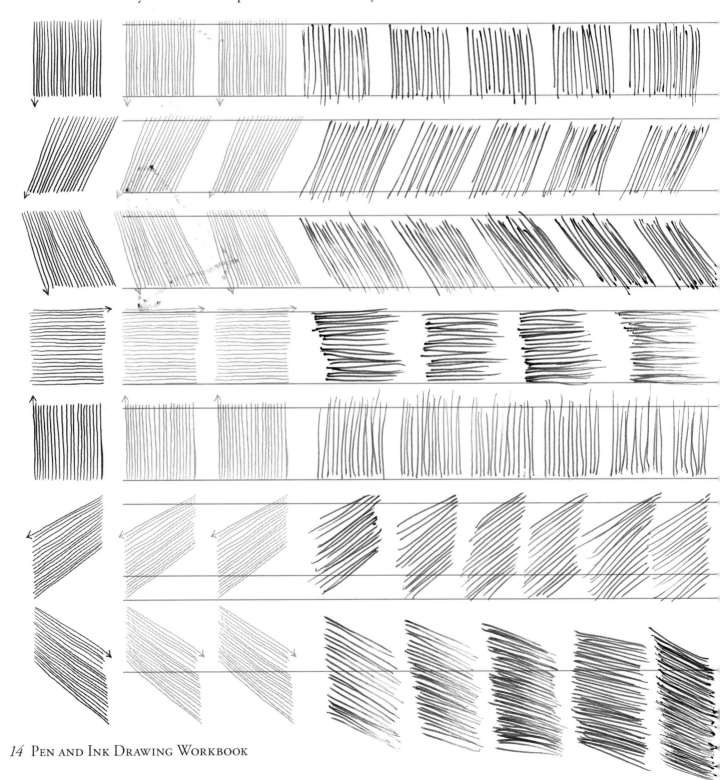

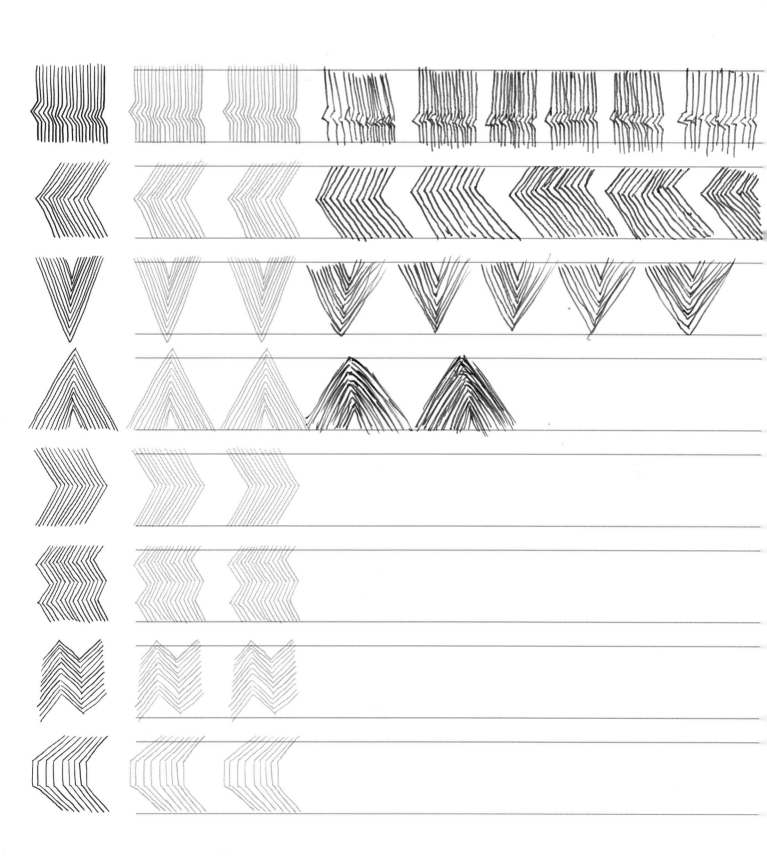

CURVED LINES

Depending on whether you are right- or left-handed you will be more comfortable drawing some lines more than others. You may also find that drawing various lines require different adjustments. It is okay to make the adjustments you feel necessary. Loosen your grip, shift your seating, or rotate the book if you need to.

TRAILING LINES

These are good drills for learning to make the general types of marks and movements you use when shading with lines. Maintain consistency in size, spacing, and direction, while trying to get a sense of the forms they could be describing.

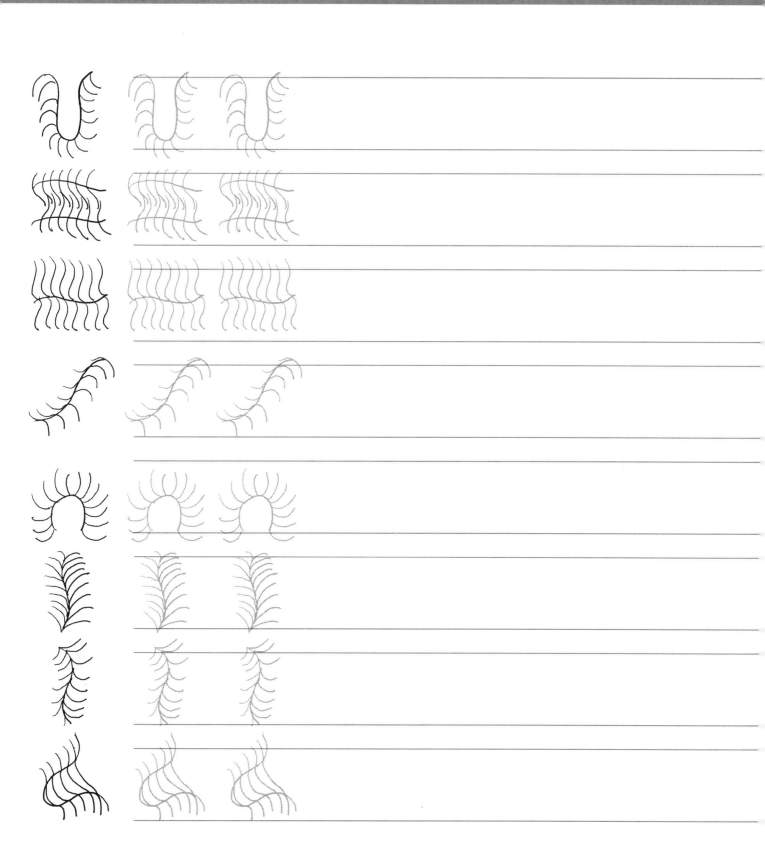

THE BASIC STROKES

These are the main types of strokes used to create most pen and ink drawings. Note that each may appear in a variety of forms. Practice until you are sufficiently proficient with each of them and are able to recognize and distinguish their use in works of other artists.

Practice   Practice   Practice

Hatching

Cross-hatching

Uneven Hatching

Curved Hatching

Scribbling

Stippling

Flowing Lines

Aim to be as proficient as possible with as many of the basic strokes as possible. Each bears its own unique characteristics, which gives you more versatility and can make your artwork more visually appealing.

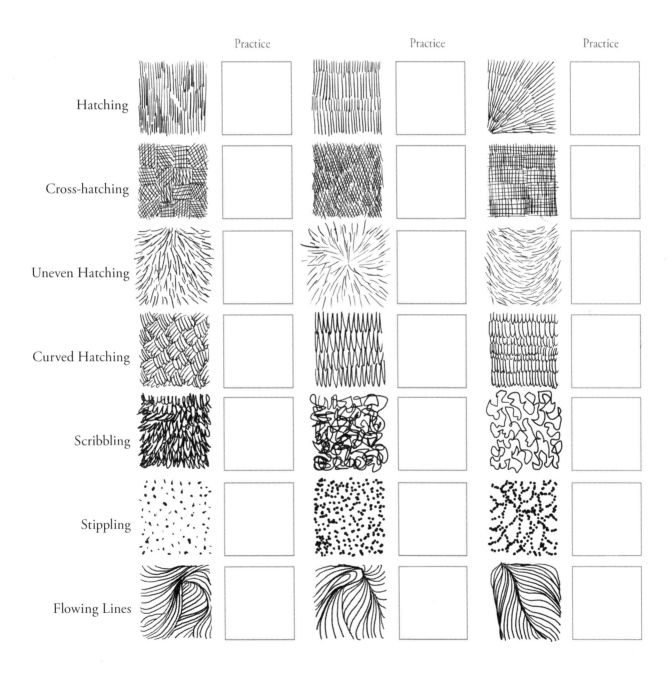

HATCHING

Hatching generally presents the least amount of challenge when learning the variations of basic strokes. Try to maintain consistency in your strokes so the overall visual effect is read clearly.

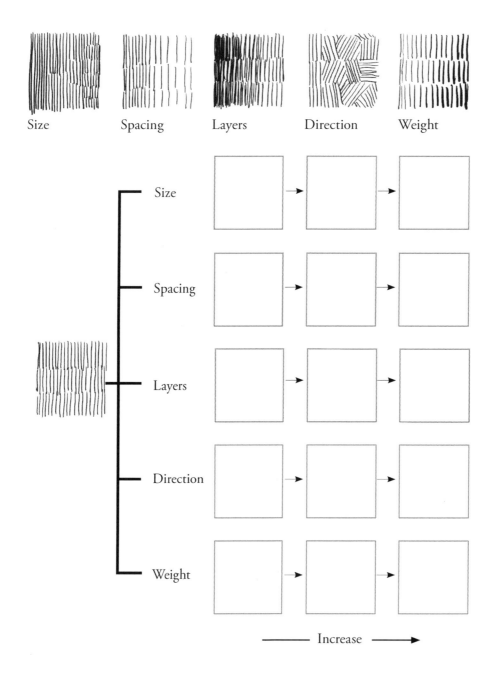

| Size | Spacing | Layers | Direction | Weight |

Size

Spacing

Layers

Direction

Weight

⟶ Increase ⟶

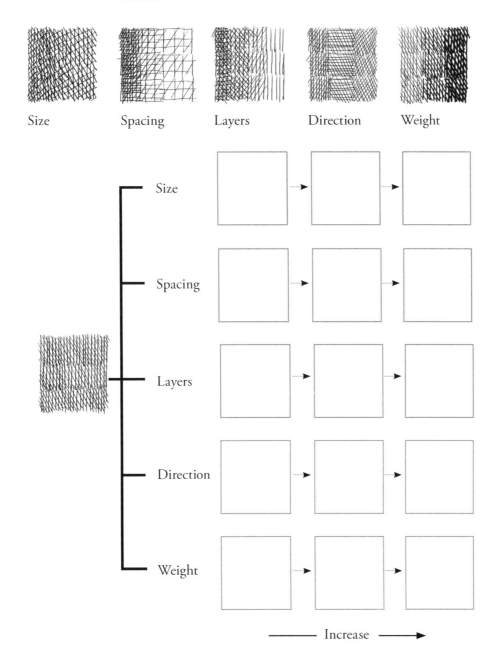

CROSS-HATCHING

Cross-hatching is perhaps the most elusive of the basic strokes for beginners. A key factor to mastering this technique is to first become proficient with using straight lines and rendering flat planes before moving on to curved surfaces and complex forms.

Size Spacing Layers Direction Weight

Size

Spacing

Layers

Direction

Weight

Increase

UNEVEN HATCHING

Uneven hatching is much more forgiving than regular hatching or cross-hatching because of the looseness of the strokes. However, with this looseness comes the challenge to maintain an overall cohesion so the desired visual effect is read clearly.

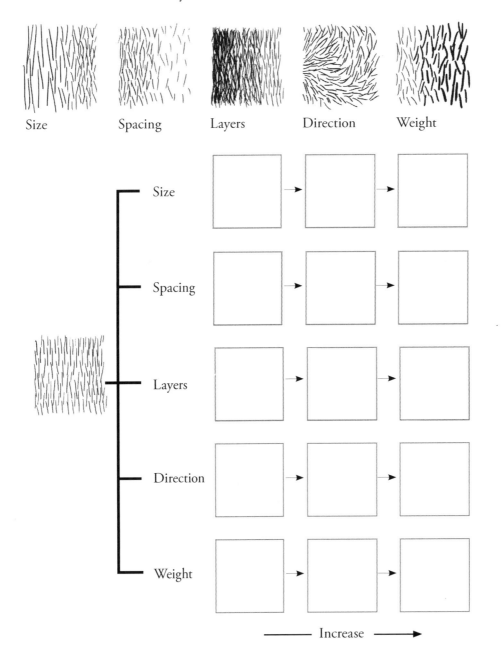

Size   Spacing   Layers   Direction   Weight

Size

Spacing

Layers

Direction

Weight

Increase ⟶

STIPPLING

The primary challenge with stippling is patience. Astounding visual effects can be created, but they mostly rely on a gradual and almost seamless shift in one or more of the variations. Consistency in pen control is also important.

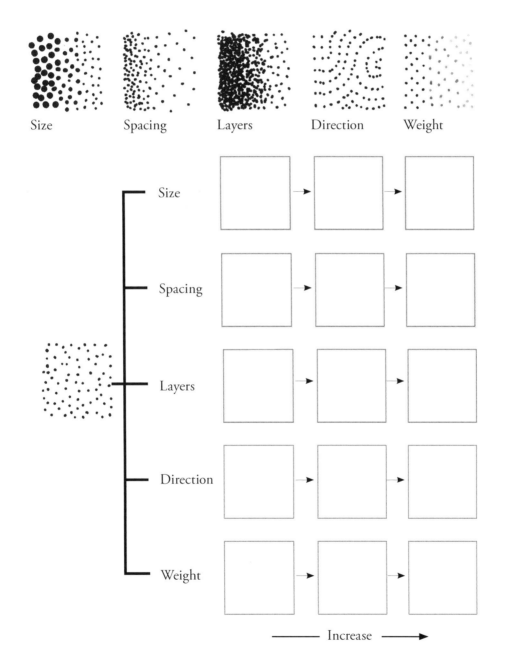

Size Spacing Layers Direction Weight

Size

Spacing

Layers

Direction

Weight

⎯⎯⎯ Increase ⎯⎯⟶

SCRIBBLING

Apart from its obvious allusion to texture, the variations of scribbling can be used to create very captivating and expressive artwork. Challenge yourself to push your pace of drawing a bit so your lines seem to spring out with a flare of fluidity and spontaneity.

Size   Spacing   Layers   Direction   Weight

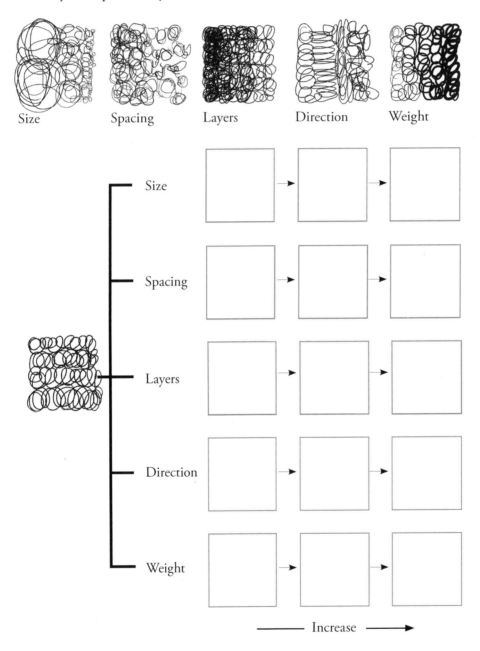

Size

Spacing

Layers

Direction

Weight

Increase

FLOWING LINES

Flowing lines can often be challenging to contain because of their length and wandering quality. Try not to press too firmly on the instrument. Instead, allow it to glide. Allow your grip to support and stabilize, but not overpower.

Size Spacing Layers Direction Weight

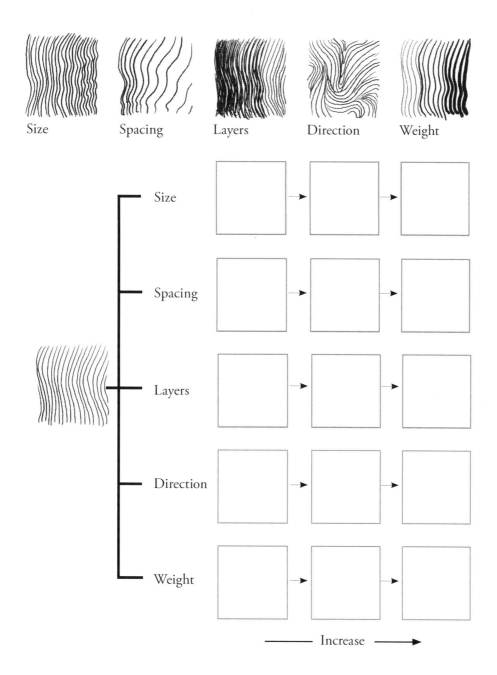

Size

Spacing

Layers

Direction

Weight

Increase ⟶

IDENTIFY VARIATIONS

Review the five common variations, then study the following drawings and try to identify the type of variations used in each. A tip is to first compare contrasting areas and deduce what that contrast is attributed to. Is it size? Is it weight? Is it spacing?

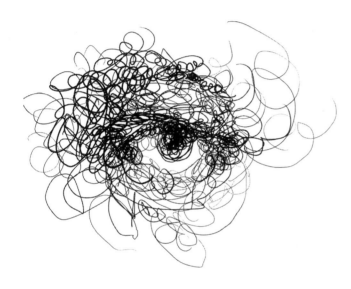

STROKE VARIATIONS

_____

_____

_____

_____

_____

STROKE VARIATIONS

_____

_____

_____

_____

_____

Different variations often occur simultaneously and in subtle shifts. Follow a value, texture, or contour from one part of the subject to another. Then try to note what changes took place. Are the strokes more spaced out, smaller, and thinner?

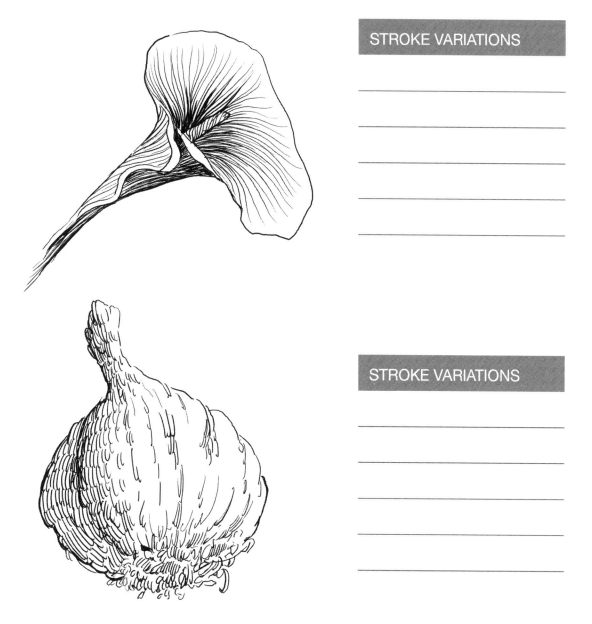

STROKE VARIATIONS

_____

_____

_____

_____

_____

STROKE VARIATIONS

_____

_____

_____

_____

_____

DISTINGUISH THE BASIC STROKES

You will naturally tend to combine the different basic strokes in a drawing because of their respective characteristics. Developing this awareness is good practice. It gives you versatility in your approach of various subjects and expands your problem-solving toolbox.

STROKES USED

- ☐ Cross-hatching
- ☐ Curved Hatching
- ☐ Flowing Lines
- ☐ Hatching
- ☐ Scribbling
- ☐ Stippling
- ☐ Uneven Hatching

STROKES USED

- ☐ Cross-hatching
- ☐ Curved Hatching
- ☐ Flowing Lines
- ☐ Hatching
- ☐ Scribbling
- ☐ Stippling
- ☐ Uneven Hatching

There will be gray areas where basic strokes that are very similar may seem indistinguishable. Don't be confused by this. The key lesson here is that you are paying attention to how the various strokes are being used based on their unique characteristics.

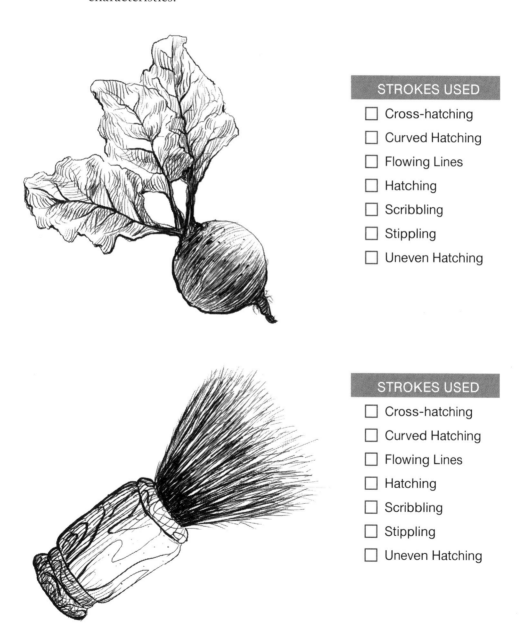

STROKES USED

☐ Cross-hatching

☐ Curved Hatching

☐ Flowing Lines

☐ Hatching

☐ Scribbling

☐ Stippling

☐ Uneven Hatching

STROKES USED

☐ Cross-hatching

☐ Curved Hatching

☐ Flowing Lines

☐ Hatching

☐ Scribbling

☐ Stippling

☐ Uneven Hatching

IDENTIFY USES OF STROKES

Review the ways of using a stroke then carefully examine
the following drawings. Remember that strokes often serve
multiple functions simultaneously. For instance, you can use
a stroke to both outline a form and also convey light and
shadow by simply varying its weight.

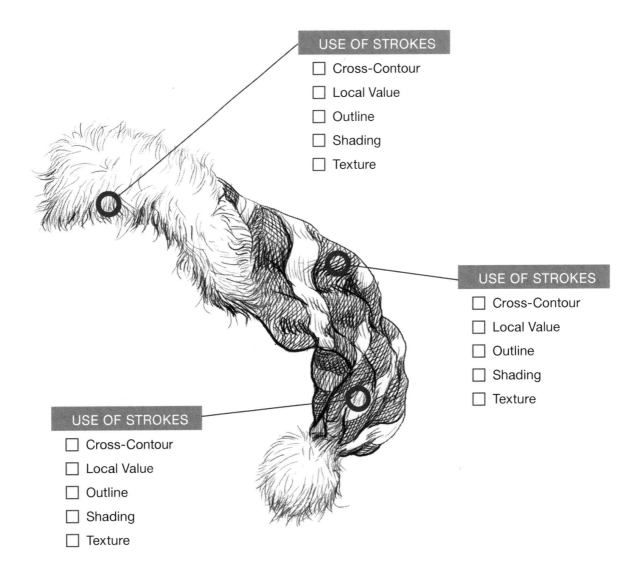

USE OF STROKES

☐ Cross-Contour

☐ Local Value

☐ Outline

☐ Shading

☐ Texture

USE OF STROKES

☐ Cross-Contour

☐ Local Value

☐ Outline

☐ Shading

☐ Texture

USE OF STROKES

☐ Cross-Contour

☐ Local Value

☐ Outline

☐ Shading

☐ Texture

The key to figuring out how strokes are used in a drawing is to study the subject and try to identify what information is being relayed to us about it. For instance, can you distinguish areas in shadow from areas in light? How was this conveyed? These are important clues to keep in mind.

USE OF STROKES

- ☐ Cross-Contour
- ☐ Local Value
- ☐ Outline
- ☐ Shading
- ☐ Texture

USE OF STROKES

- ☐ Cross-Contour
- ☐ Local Value
- ☐ Outline
- ☐ Shading
- ☐ Texture

USE OF STROKES

- ☐ Cross-Contour
- ☐ Local Value
- ☐ Outline
- ☐ Shading
- ☐ Texture

2

Shading

The exercises of this section are based on chapter two of *Pen & Ink Drawing: A Simple Guide*. Shading can infuse life into your drawings. It can add depth, mass, volume, and visual interest. However, it is a bane of many beginners' drawing experience and is often perceived to be more complicated than it really is. The key to understanding shading is to start with the basics. Establish a solid foundation based on the fundamental principles. This section lays out a series of exercises designed to develop and refine the essential ink-rendering skills and develop your understanding of the core concepts: value, shading, and light and shadow. There are over 40 exercises in this section and they are all tailored to help take your shading to the next level.

VARYING LINE-WEIGHT

By simply varying the thickness and thinness of lines, we can make them significantly more expressive and create a variety of visual effects. The key is to carefully vary the pressure you place on the drawing instrument.

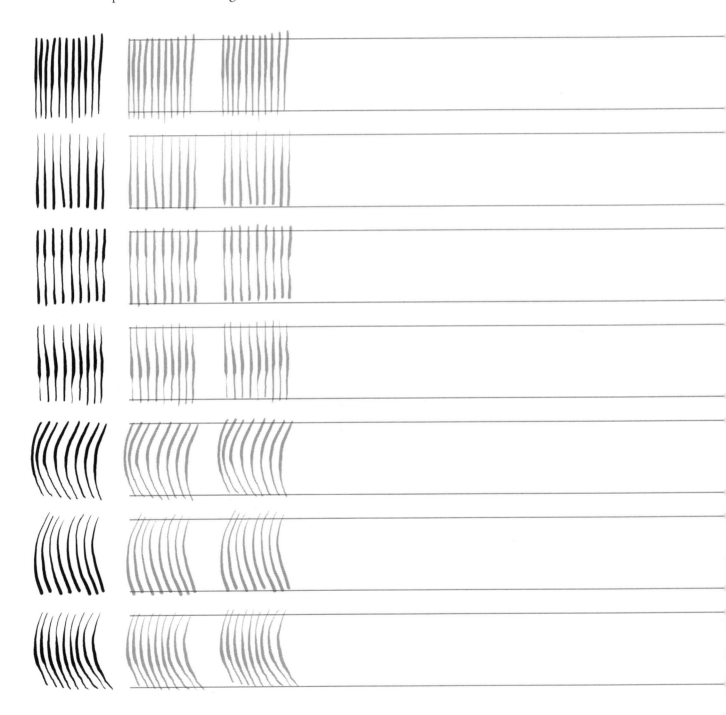

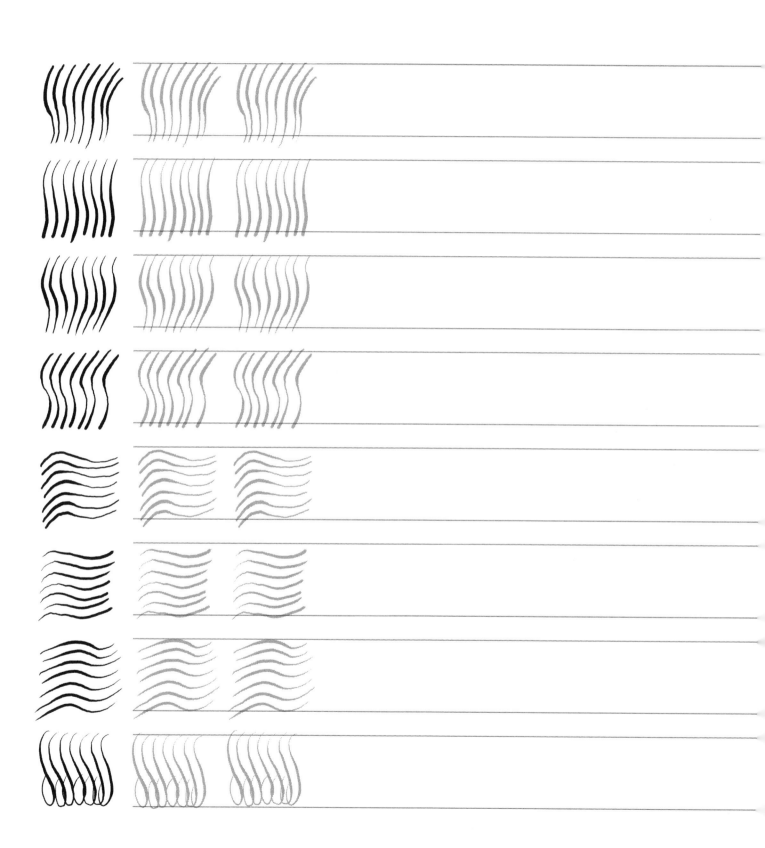

VARYING LINE-WEIGHT

A simple variation in the weight of a contour can make a subject appear to come to life with volume, mass, and movement. Practice correlating variation in line-weight with the light and shadow, mass, and three-dimensional shape of the subject.

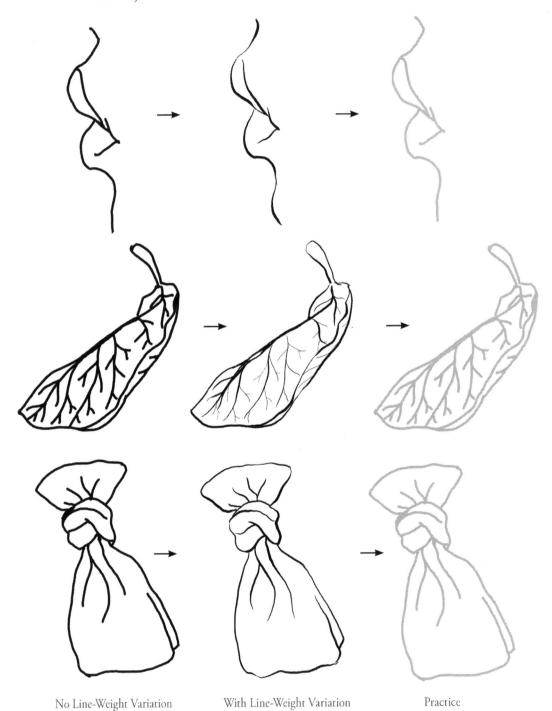

No Line-Weight Variation   With Line-Weight Variation   Practice

With the following exercise, determine the direction of a light source in relation to each subject, and then adjust the weight of your lines based on where the areas of light and shadow will be.

No Line-Weight Variation   Practice

CROSS-CONTOUR LINES

Cross-contour lines are a critical aspect of pen and ink drawing because they can convey so much information about a subject. They describe form, texture, value, mass, light and shadow, and more. Try to envision the three-dimensional shape of subjects before drawing them.

No Cross-Contour Lines   With Cross-Contour Lines   Practice

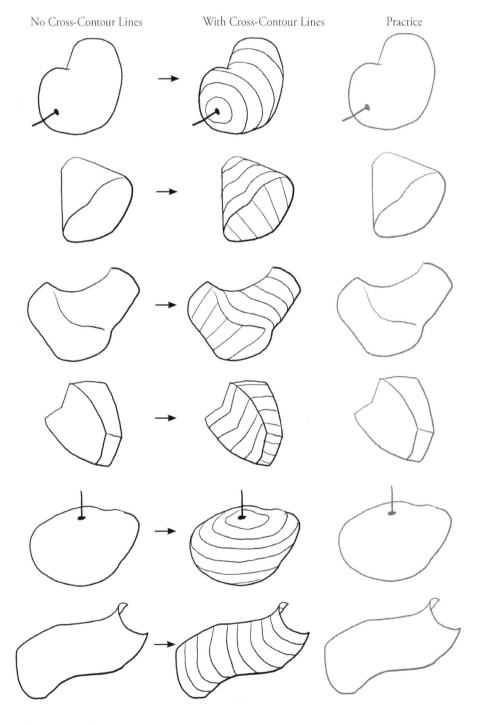

Apply cross-contour lines to these forms.

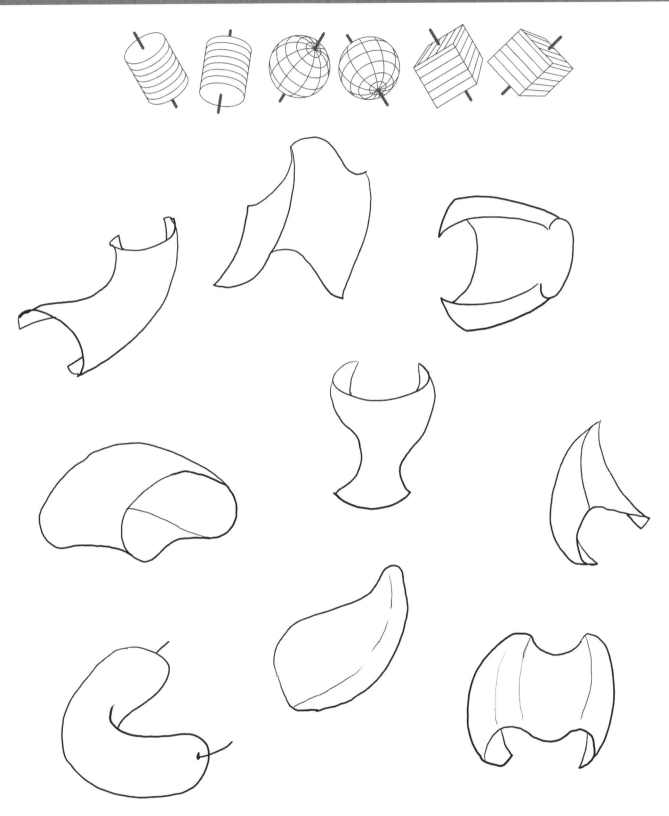

Apply cross-contour lines to these forms.

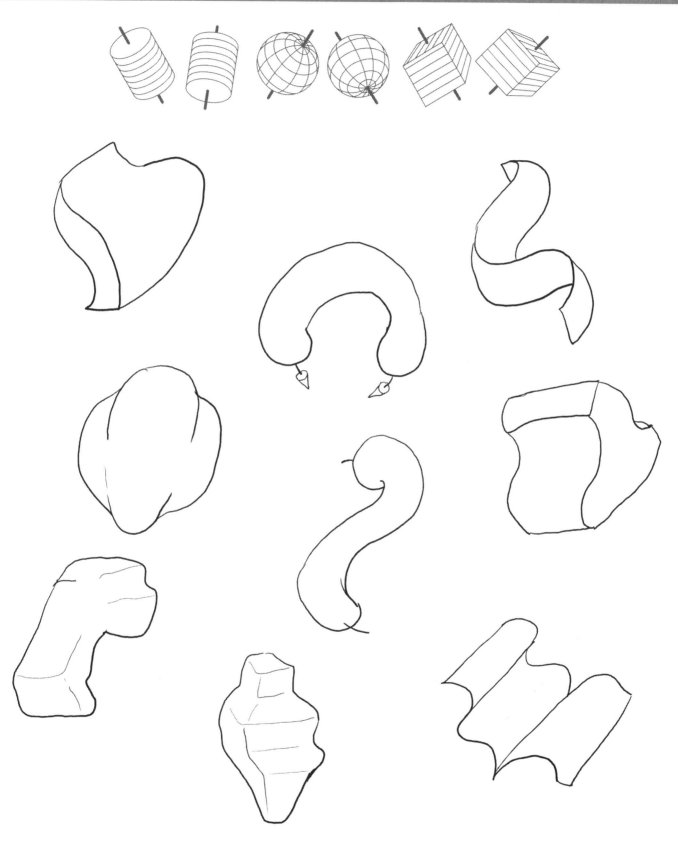

Apply cross-contour lines to these forms.

CREATING EVEN VALUE

Creating and maintaining the value of a given area is important in drawing. For instance, areas in light, shadow, and half-shadow should be easily distinguished and should maintain their respective values. Be aware of the pen-control adjustments you make for each area and keep them consistent.

Practice

Hatching

Cross-hatching

Uneven Hatching

Curved Hatching

Scribbling

Stippling

Flowing Lines

The challenge of this exercise is to maintain the designated value within each section, while working within the irregularities in the shape of each.

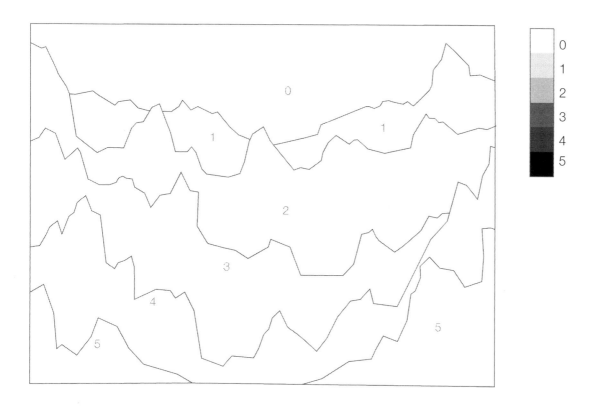

6-STEP VALUE SCALE

Creating value scales is one of the most invaluable exercises in drawing. With pen and ink drawing, you will find that each type of basic stroke presents its own challenge. Experiment with the variations to see what types of adjustments are needed in order to convey value change.

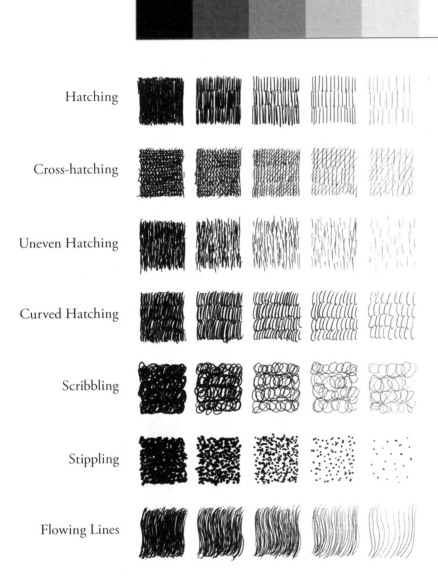

Hatching

Cross-hatching

Uneven Hatching

Curved Hatching

Scribbling

Stippling

Flowing Lines

Hatching

Cross-hatching

Uneven Hatching

Curved Hatching

Scribbling

Stippling

Flowing Lines

IDENTIFYING VALUES

A critical skill in drawing is being able to identify and
distinguish values. This helps you to assess and understand
the overall value pattern of a subject. First, start by comparing
the most contrasting values then determine the intermediate
values.

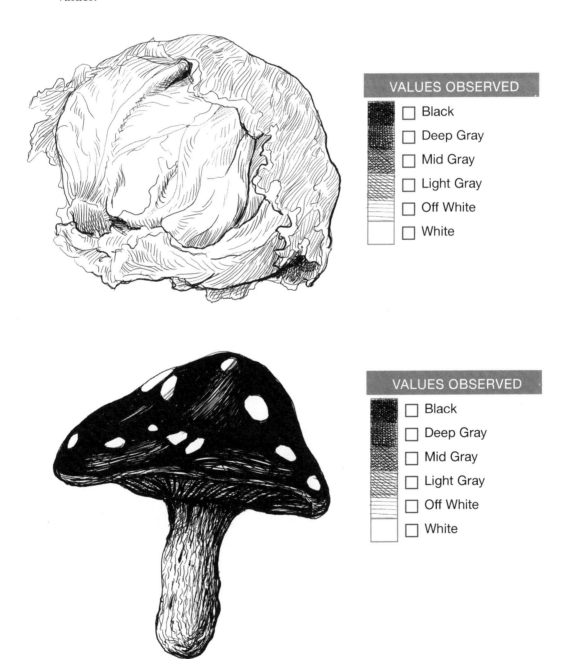

VALUES OBSERVED

☐ Black
☐ Deep Gray
☐ Mid Gray
☐ Light Gray
☐ Off White
☐ White

VALUES OBSERVED

☐ Black
☐ Deep Gray
☐ Mid Gray
☐ Light Gray
☐ Off White
☐ White

It is not necessary to distinguish every nuance of value.
Sometimes categorizing values you observe into simple groups
of three or four is best.

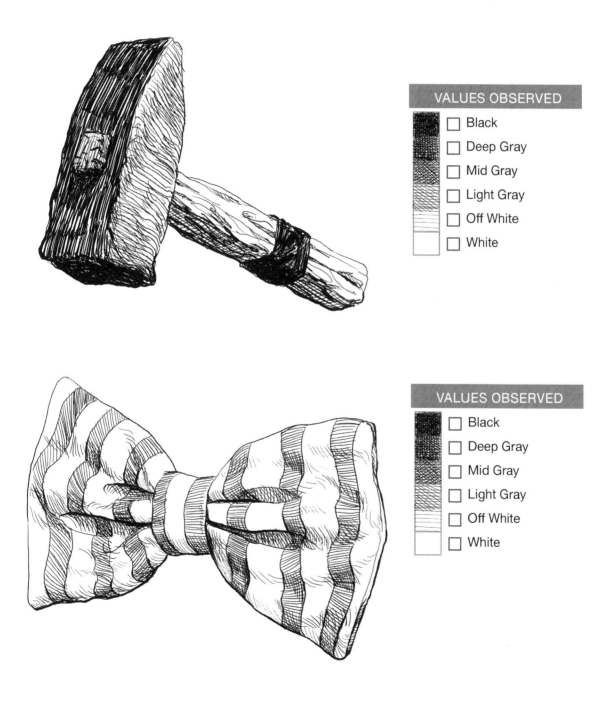

VALUES OBSERVED
- ☐ Black
- ☐ Deep Gray
- ☐ Mid Gray
- ☐ Light Gray
- ☐ Off White
- ☐ White

VALUES OBSERVED
- ☐ Black
- ☐ Deep Gray
- ☐ Mid Gray
- ☐ Light Gray
- ☐ Off White
- ☐ White

9-STEP VALUE SCALE

There is generally no need for more than around six values to effectively render a subject, but creating a 9-step value scale can be a fun and challenging exercise. It requires making more nuanced changes in value and working at a more moderate pace to avoid reaching extreme values too quickly.

3-Steps

6-Steps

9-Steps

Hatching

Cross-hatching

Uneven Hatching

Curved Hatching

Scribbling

Stippling

Flowing Lines

BLENDING VALUES

Smoothly blending values is an essential skill in drawing. The applications range from modeling three-dimensional forms to conveying depth, mass, and more. When blending values, leave the deepest and lightest values for last and focus on the middle value transitions first.

Practice

Hatching

Cross-hatching

Uneven Hatching

Curved Hatching

Scribbling

Stippling

Flowing Lines

RATE OF GRADATION

Sometimes the nature of the light source, or the size and shape of the form, affects the rate of the transition between light and shadow values. To account for this, you should practice to control how fast or slow the values shift between light and deep values.

Practice

Practice

RANGE OF GRADATION

Values won't always change from dark entirely to light or vice versa. Depending on the local value of that area or its position with respect to the light source, values may change very little. This exercise will help you to make subtle transitions in value.

Practice

Deep to Deep Value

Deep to Mid-Value

Deep to Light Value

Mid to Mid-Value

Mid to Light Value

Light to Light Value

DIRECTION OF GRADATION

Although in practice we tend to grade values in a straight line, in reality most of our gradations will occur in various directions. This exercise provides practice in gradating values in different directions determined by the shape of the forms.

Example   Practice

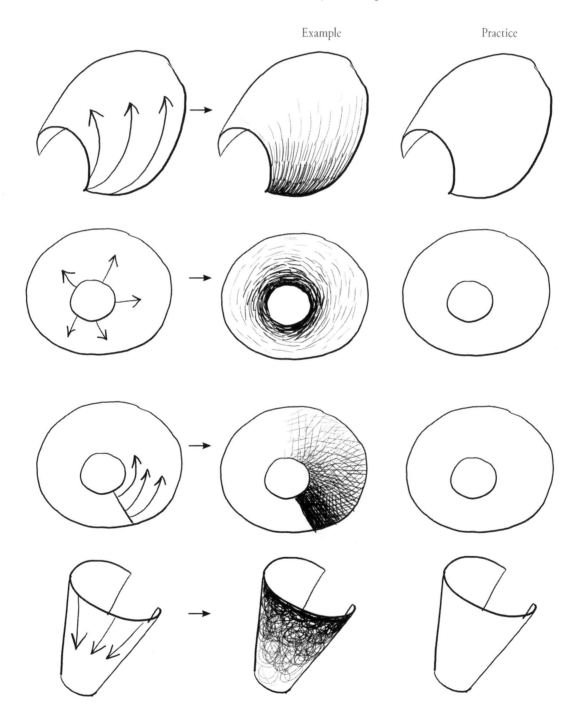

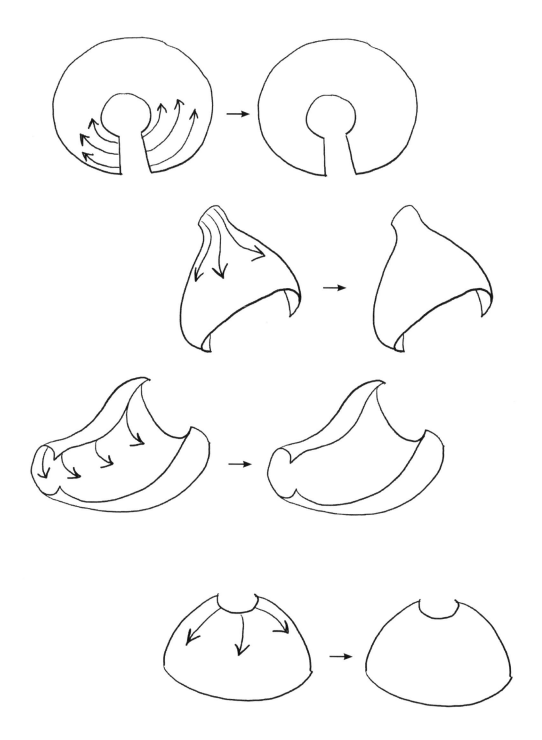

Apply gradation (from shadow to light) to these forms in
the directions indicated.

REVEALING PLANES

Understanding the underlying structure of forms enables us
to sense the position of their planes. With this understanding,
we can have a stronger command over rendering light and
shadow because we can see how the value pattern is formed.

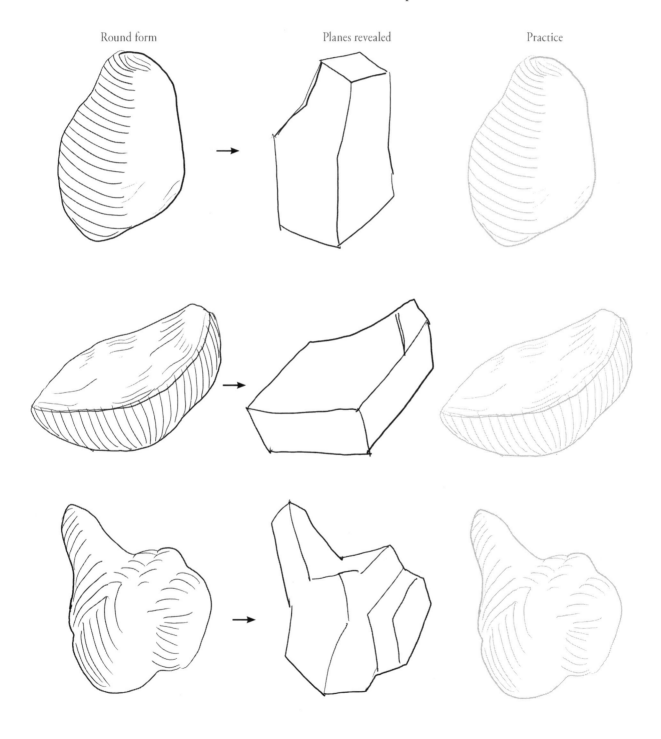

Round form   Planes revealed   Practice

The key to this exercise is to look for where the major shifts in value occur. Major plane changes generally coincide with major value changes.

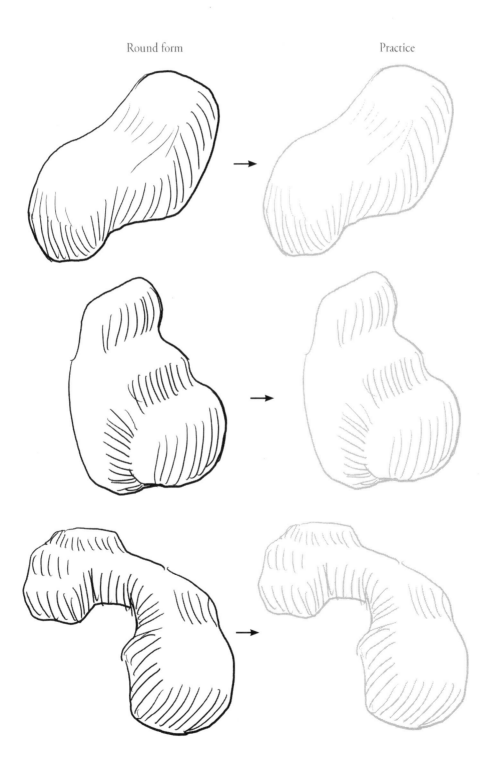

Round form   Practice

LINE DIRECTION AND STRUCTURE

This is one of the unique characteristics of shading with line: You can keep the collective value of a group of lines the same while changing their direction to convey the structure of a form. Compare the two cubes to see this effect. Then practice with the compound form below.

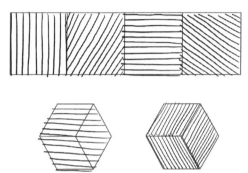

Structure not emphasized   Structure emphasized

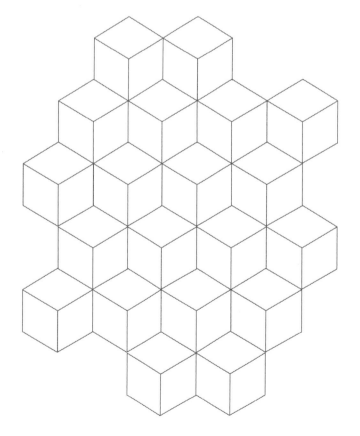

In both drawings the overall value conveyed by the strokes
stays the same, although their direction changes to follow the
cross-contour of the forms. Try to master this technique. It is
critical to your success in pen and ink drawing. The goal is to
keep your lines consistent regardless of the area they describe.

Example   Practice

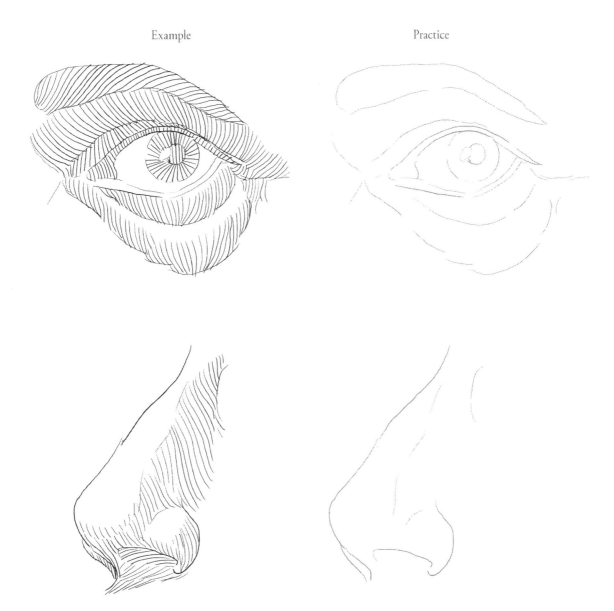

3-VALUE SHADING

Blocks are an excellent model for studying light and shadow
and learning to render values based on planes. With this
exercise, you limit your shading to three values. Each form
is oriented differently towards the lights source and the light
and shadow values are placed accordingly.

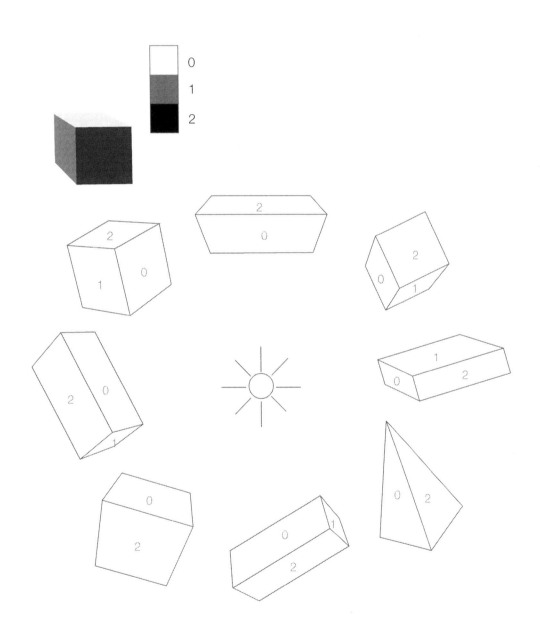

Use the numbers as a guide to assigning values to each plane.

SHADING BLOCK FORMS

This exercise expands the value range to six values and increases the complexity of the forms. However, the same basic principle applies, so determining the value for each plane is not as elusive as you may think. Study the orientation of each plane with respect to the light source.

Use the numbers as a guide to assigning values to each plane.

This is similar to *Exercise 2.25*, except the forms are not
suspended around the light source. Study the position of each
form and the orientation of its planes with respect to the light
source to determine where the values will be placed.

This is similar to *Exercise 2.27,* except the forms are not suspended around the light source. Study the position of each form and the orientation of its planes with respect to the light source to determine where the values will be placed.

SHADING BLOCK FORMS

This exercise takes things a bit further by placing a large dominant form at center-stage. The dominant form will set the tone for the smaller forms placed around it. Identical forms placed at different positions around the dominant form can have different value patterns based on the amount of light each receives. Shade in the values by numbers.

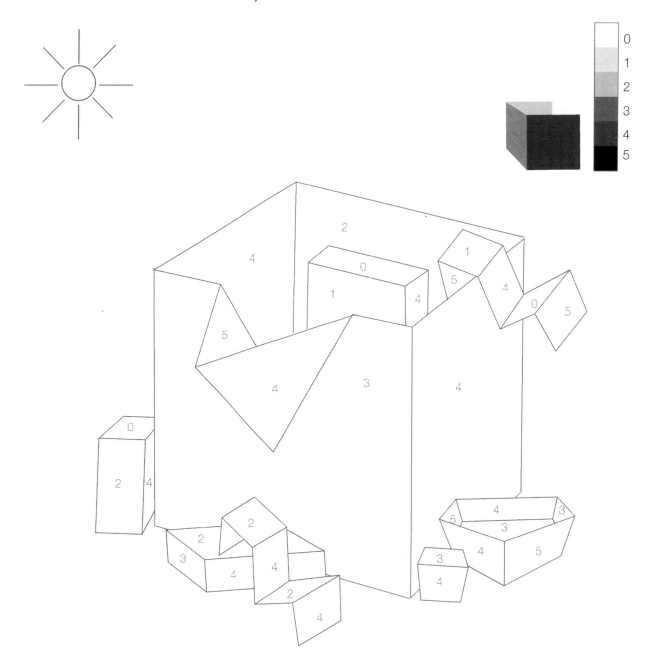

This is very similar to the previous exercise, except without the numbers provided as a guide. Study the position of each form and the orientation of its planes with respect to the light source to determine where the values will be placed.

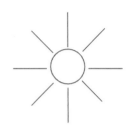

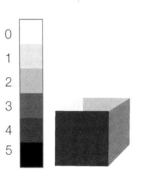

SHADING CURVED SURFACES

With curved surfaces, we use a similar principle; however, values don't change sharply. There is a seamless transition between light and shadow. Leave lightest and deepest areas for last and plan your value assignments before rendering.

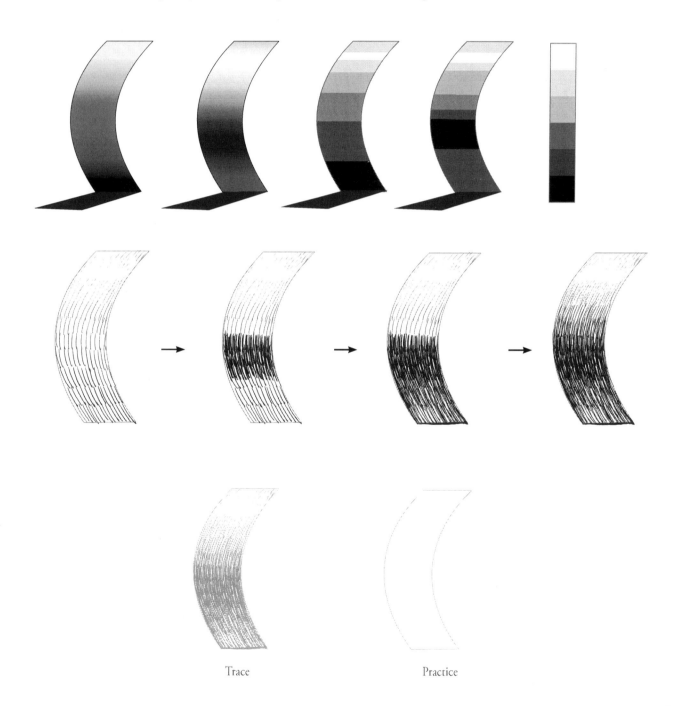

Trace

Practice

PEN&INK
DRAWING
WORKBOOK

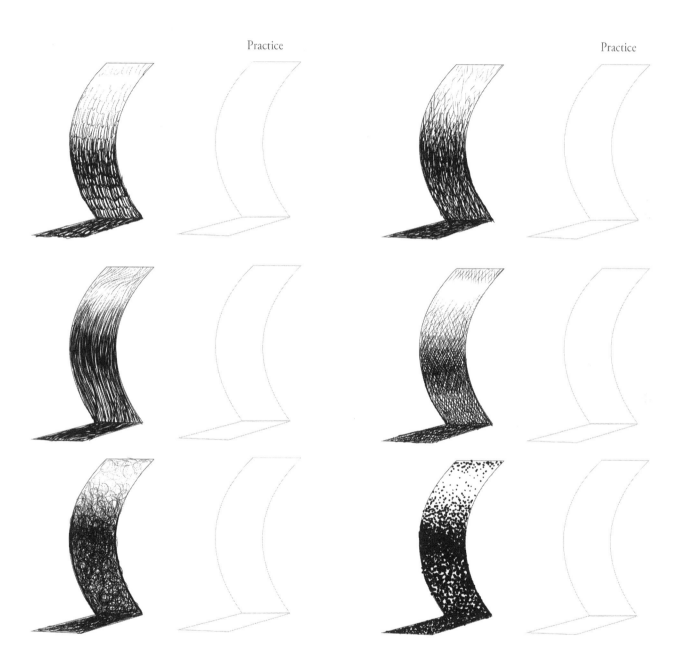

Practice

Practice

SHADING CYLINDERS

The same principle applies here as in *Exercise 2.33*. A cylinder is essentially a curved surface wrapped in a circle. Simple forms are wonderful models to practice your shading technique on because you can reduce virtually all subjects to simple forms in some way.

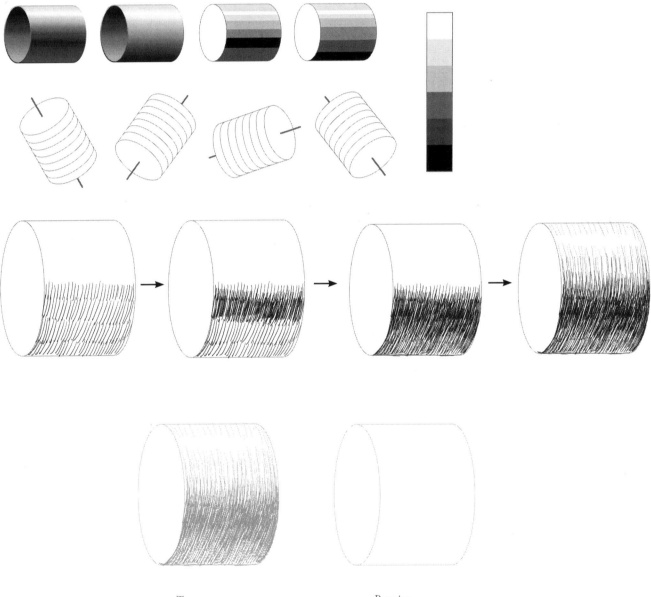

Trace

Practice

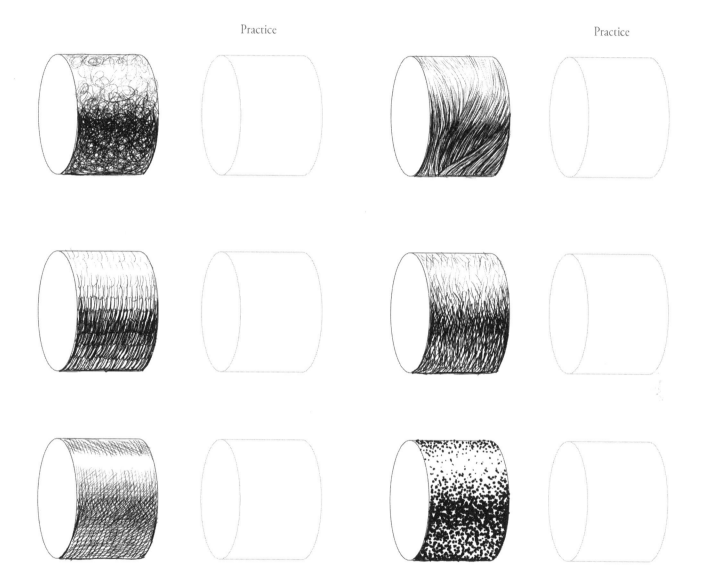

Practice   Practice

SHADING SPHERES

A sphere presents a unique challenge; you are essentially shading a curving surface that diverges from a single point and then converges to another. Similar to *Exercise 2.19*, think of shading spheres as an exercise in controlling the direction of your gradation to diverge away from, or converge toward, a point.

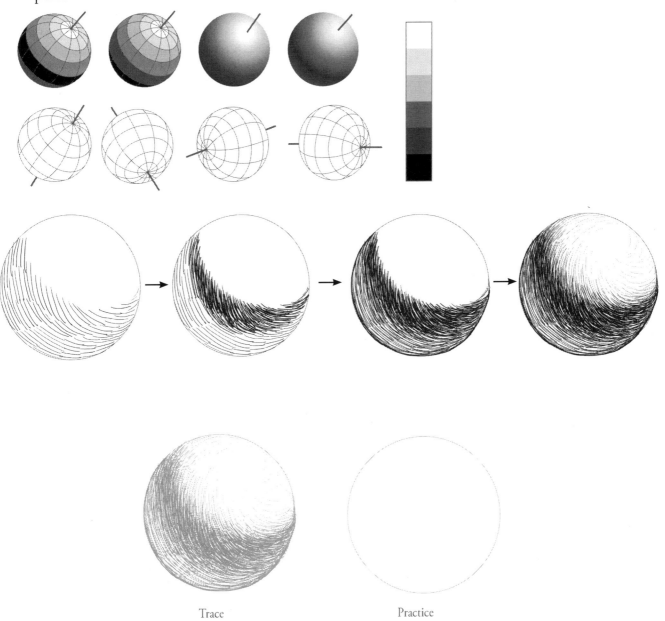

Trace   Practice

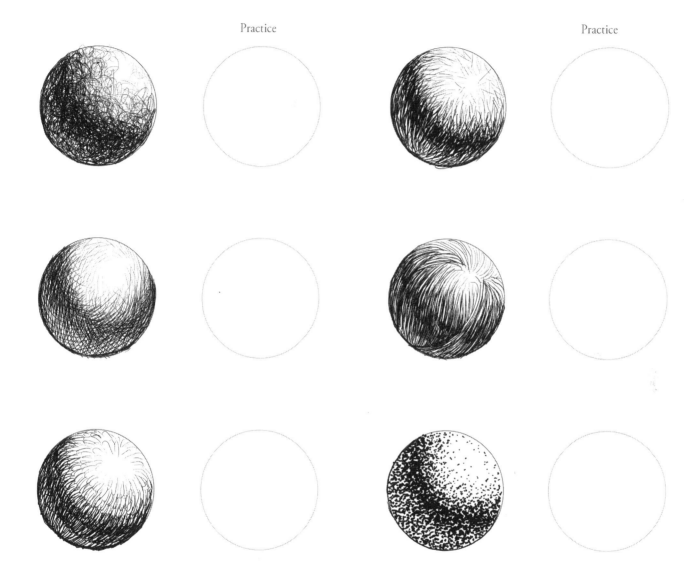

Practice

Practice

SIMPLE FORMS COMPOSITION

The challenge here is to keep the overall value pattern consistent on all the forms so that it is understood that the light source originates from the upper left. Study the position and orientation of each form with respect to the light source to determine where the values will be placed.

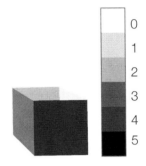

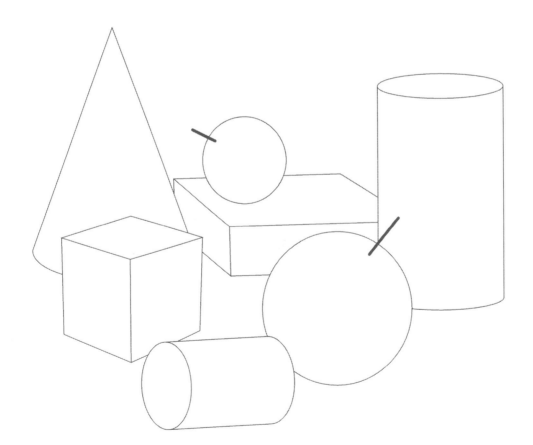

Here, the forms are a bit more complex than in the previous exercise, however, upon closer inspection you will quickly realize the same principles apply. Study the position and orientation of each form with respect to the light source to determine where the values will be placed.

LOCAL VALUE

You will often be confronted with the challenge of distinguishing local values. To distinguish one form as inherently deeper or lighter in value than another, individual value-range limits must be established and maintained. This exercise helps you with practicing just that. Shade by numbers to complete the exercise.

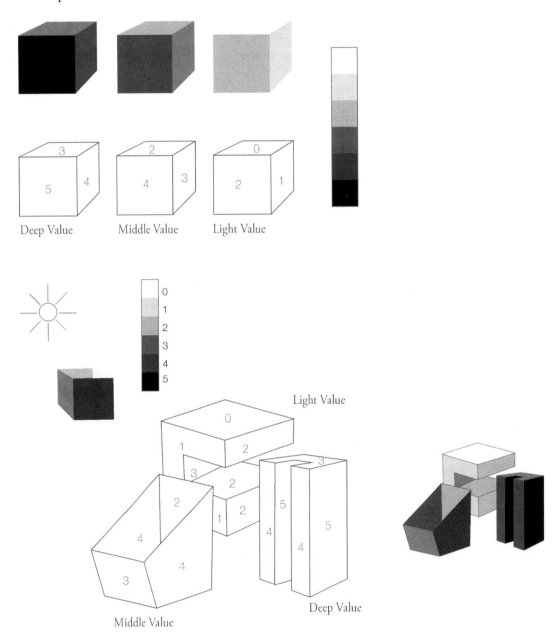

Deep Value   Middle Value   Light Value

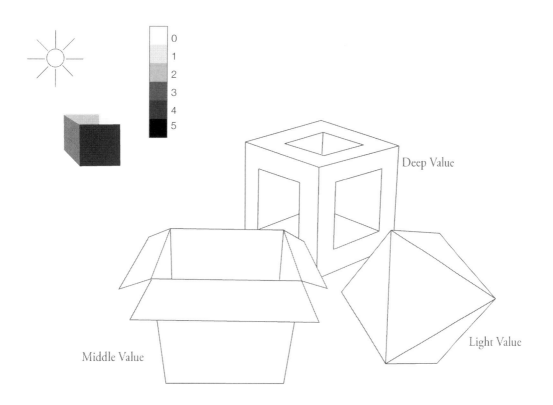

Deep Value

Middle Value

Light Value

Render each form based on the designated local value and its position in relation to the light source.

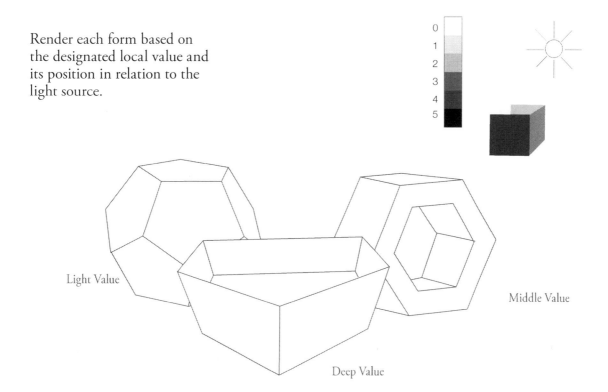

Light Value

Deep Value

Middle Value

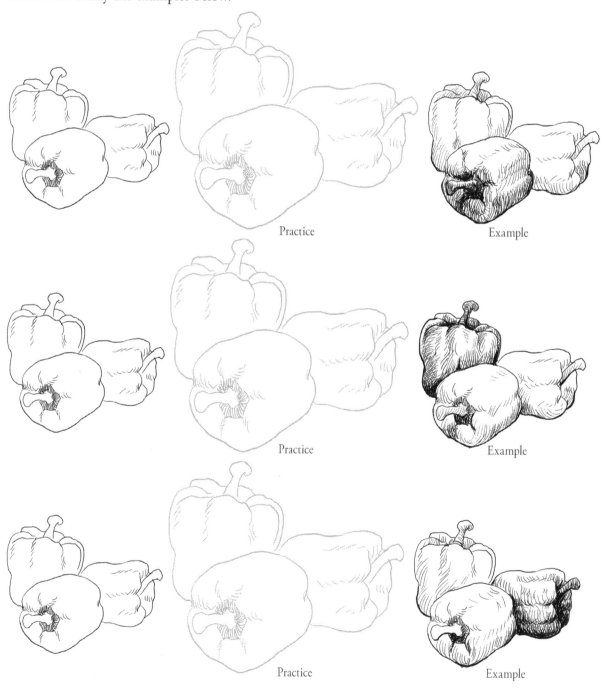

DETERMINE FOCAL AREA

Creating emphasis is a powerful way to take creative control over your drawing and an effective means of self-expression. Take time to study your subject or composition, then determine where will be your area of focus and how you will make it so. Study the examples below.

Practice

Example

Practice

Example

Practice

Example

This is similar to the previous exercise. Redraw the composition but emphasize a different item in each drawing. To create emphasis you can consider adjusting the amount of details, line-weight, or rendering of light and shadow.

Emphasize Left

Emphasize Middle

Emphasize Right

COMPOUND FORMS

Complex forms can sometimes be intimidating; however, they can be tamed by visualizing them as a combination of simple forms. This exercise helps you to understand that complex forms are generally nothing more than a group of simple forms fused together.

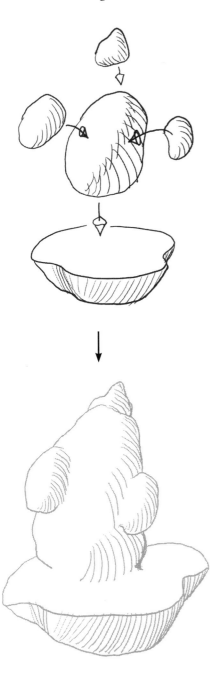

Trace

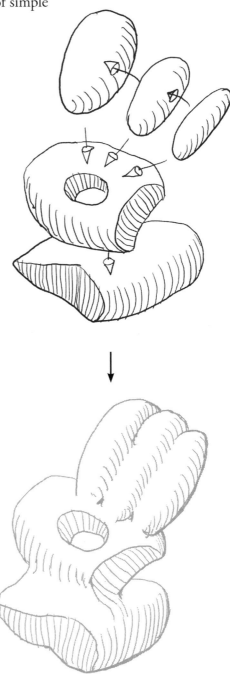

Trace

This is similar to the previous exercise. Fuse the simple forms together and create a new compound form. Think about what planes are facing each other and then ensure the value pattern of the light and shadow areas is consistent across all the forms.

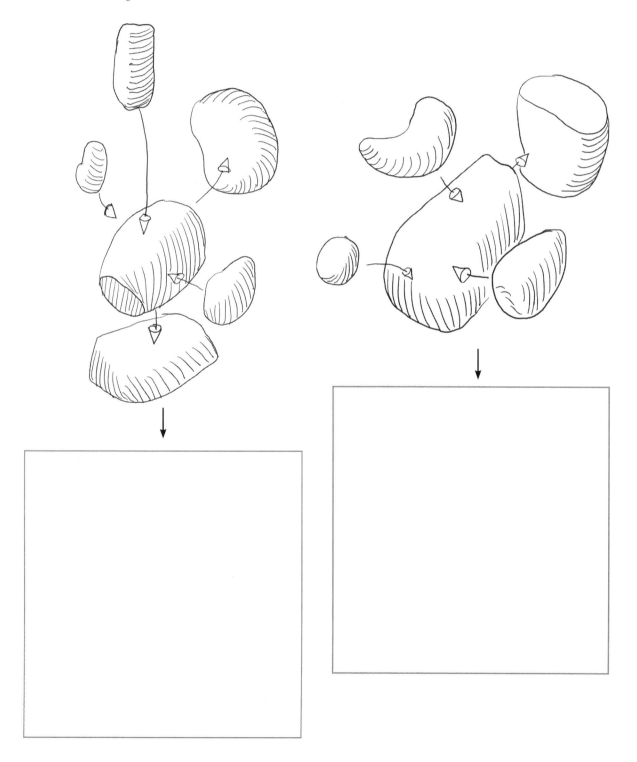

3

Simulating Texture

The exercises of this section are based on chapter four of *Pen & Ink Drawing: A Simple Guide.* The bold quality of pen and ink lends itself well to creating stunning textures and often results in students feeling a bit intimidated. The process does not have to be elusive, and with adequate practice, patience, and the help of a simple system, creating captivating textures will be well within reach. This section breaks down the process into simple exercises that focus on the essential elements and principles, before applying them together on rendering three-dimensional forms.

TEXTURE PATTERNS

All textures are based on some type of pattern. With pen and ink drawing, dots, lines, shapes, and values can be used as your building blocks. Combined with the five variations, these building blocks can be used to create hundreds of captivating textures.

Practice   Practice

Stipple Patterns

Line Patterns

Shape Patterns

Combined Patterns

Combined Patterns

Note that even subtle differences in a pattern can result in dramatically different textures. Even with identical shapes, simply varying the direction or spacing slightly creates new textures.

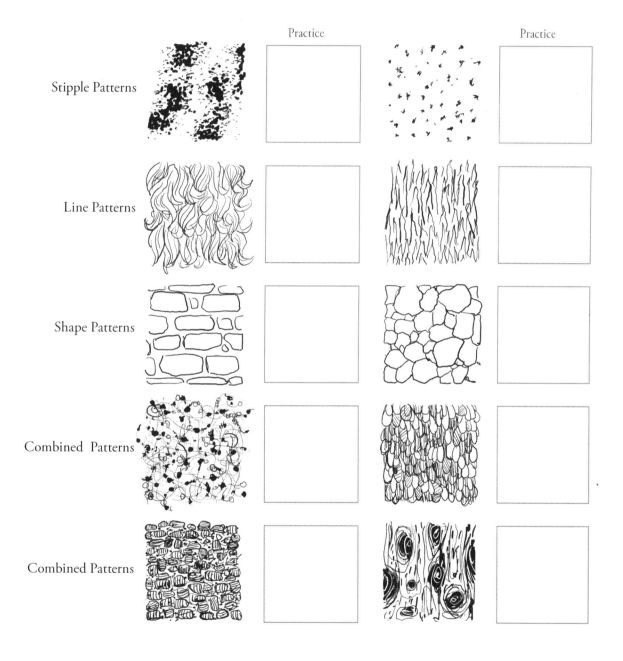

Practice

Practice

Stipple Patterns

Line Patterns

Shape Patterns

Combined Patterns

Combined Patterns

TEXTURE CHART

Get into the habit of collecting as many textures as possible and store them in a texture chart. Draw inspiration from your environment, photographs, books, videos, or from other artists.

Practice   Practice

Practice these textures and use the liberty to modify them and create new textures. Make notes on the type of subjects each texture evokes or inspires. One texture can be used for several different subjects with only minor modifications.

Practice   Practice

CREATE TEXTURE PATTERNS

As you study and practice, keep building your own library of patterns and textures. Challenge yourself in various ways. For instance, you could start with only one building block and come up with as many patterns as you can. After this exercise, create more variations by mixing the building blocks in different combinations.

Stipple Patterns

Line Patterns

Shape Patterns

Combined Patterns

Combined Patterns

CREATE A TEXTURE CHART

Eventually, you will easily have tens of textures to use as reference for depicting subjects and creating new artworks. Sometimes it will be important to make notes on how you created a particular texture. This is helpful, especially, when the process involves a series of steps that are not immediately apparent.

TEXTURED CONTOURS

In this exercise, you will add texture to the outline of each form. This enables you to see the effect on the way we perceive a form when a texture defines its outline. Ignore the interior space, and apply the texture to the outline only.

Example   Practice

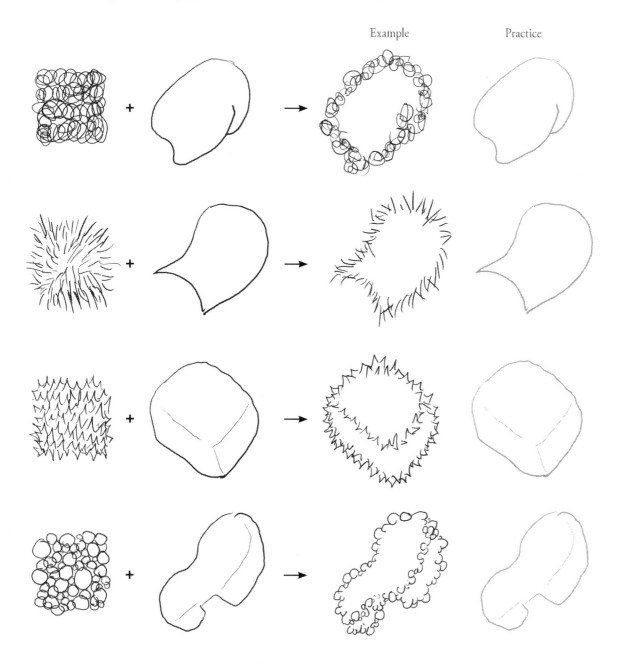

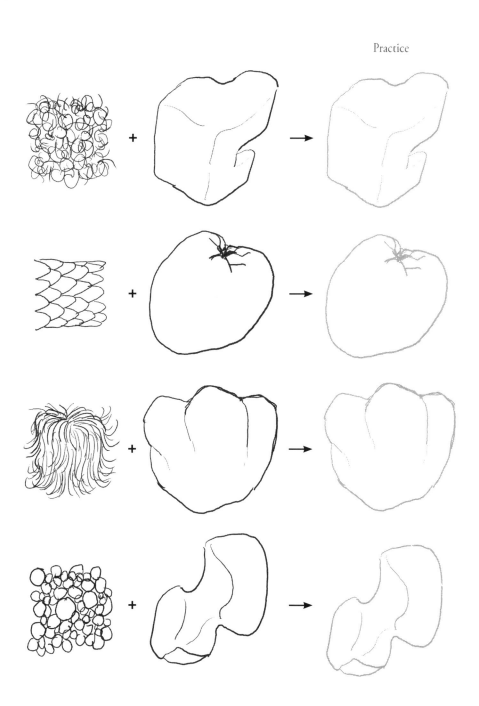

Practice

Apply the designated texture to the outline of each form.

TEXTURE FOLLOWS FORM

Think of textures on forms in the same way you see lines of latitude and longitude follow the curvature of a globe. The texture not only describes the surface quality of the form, but also accentuates its three-dimensional shape, volume, and structure.

Example   Practice

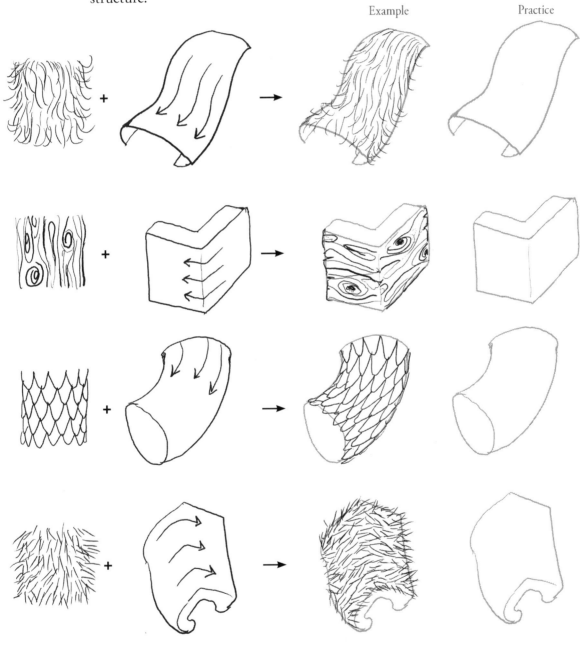

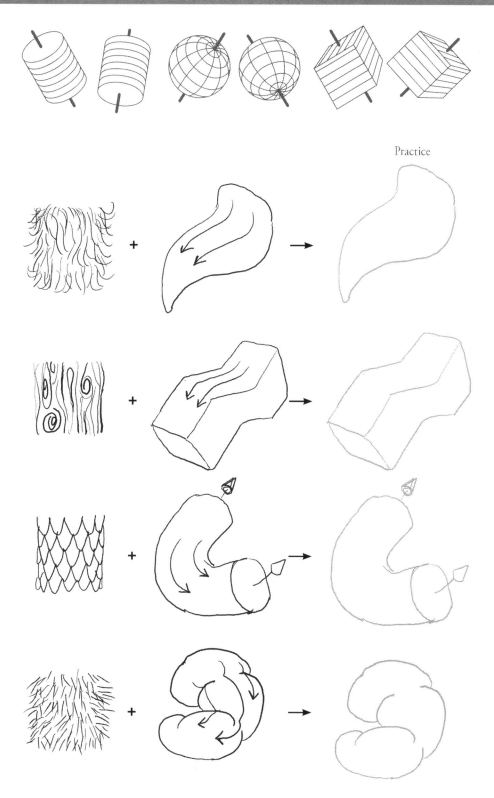

Practice

Apply the designated texture to the cross-contour of each form.

TEXTURE FOLLOWS FORM

This exercise demonstrates what happens when the texture is directly applied in a flat manner without regard for the structure of the form it covers. Modify the texture so it appropriately follows the form in each example.

Texture doesn't follow the form   Texture follows the form   Practice

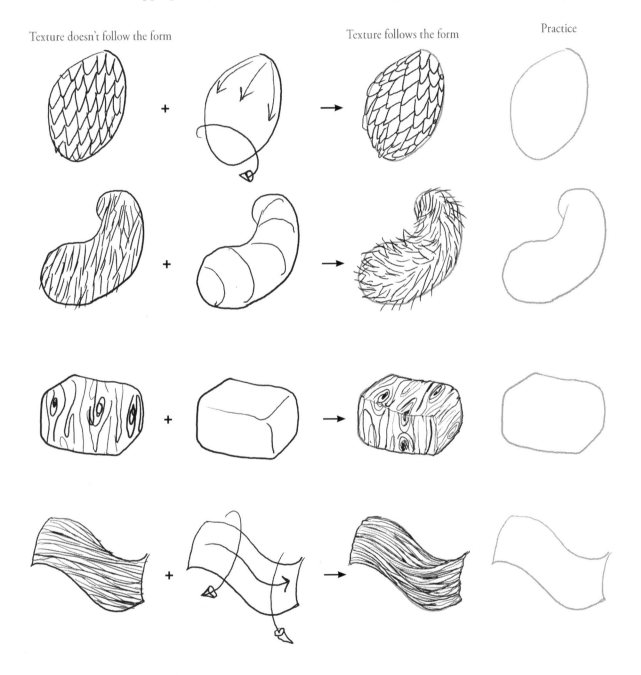

Texture doesn't follow the form   Practice

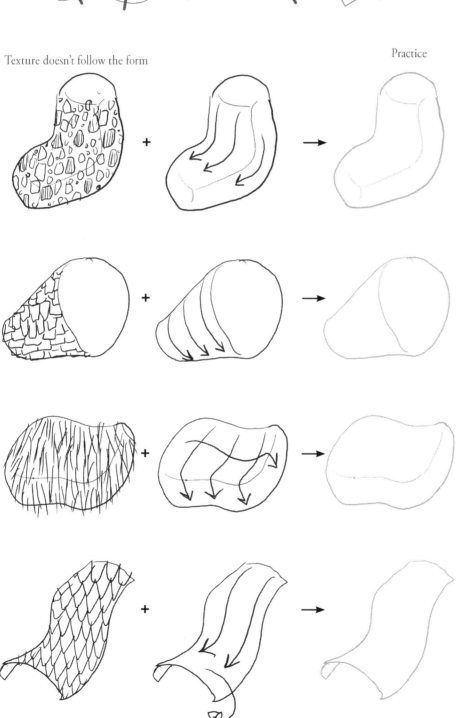

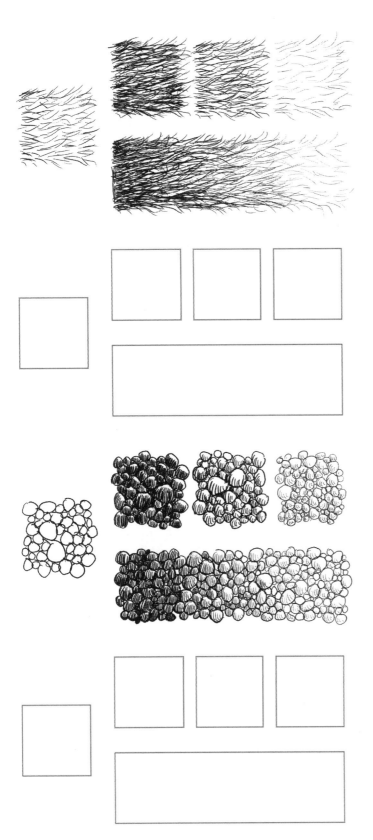

TEXTURE VALUE SCALE

In this exercise, it is important to take things up a notch and finally breathe life into your textures. This is perhaps the most challenging aspect of rendering textures. You are modifying the texture to convey the effect of light and shadow, while maintaining its respective characteristics. It must remain consistently recognizable in areas of light, shadow, and half-shadow.

EXERCISE 3.14   Shading Textures

It is better to complete the step-wise value scale first in order to isolate and practice the different value areas. After, having learned the variations you need to make, it will be much easier to apply the blended effect.

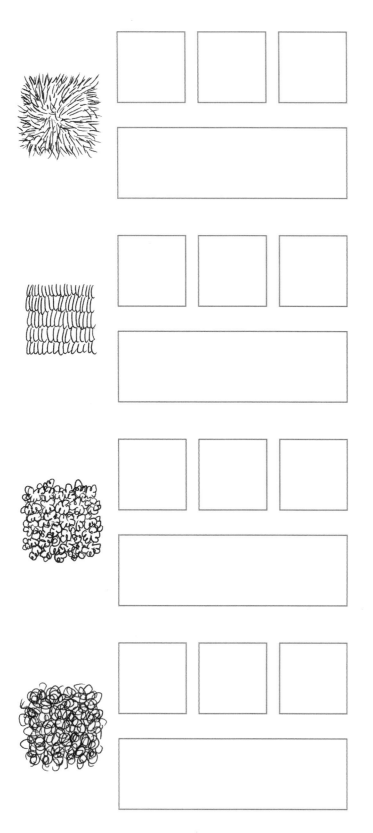

TEXTURE VALUE SCALE

Different textures will sometimes require different approaches in conveying light and shadow. Some may need an overlay of hatch marks to deepen their value while others may only need a few added layers of the same pattern.

Remember to explore the five stroke variations in conveying the gradation of value between light and shadow. Adding layers may help to deepen value, while increasing spacing may help to lighten it.

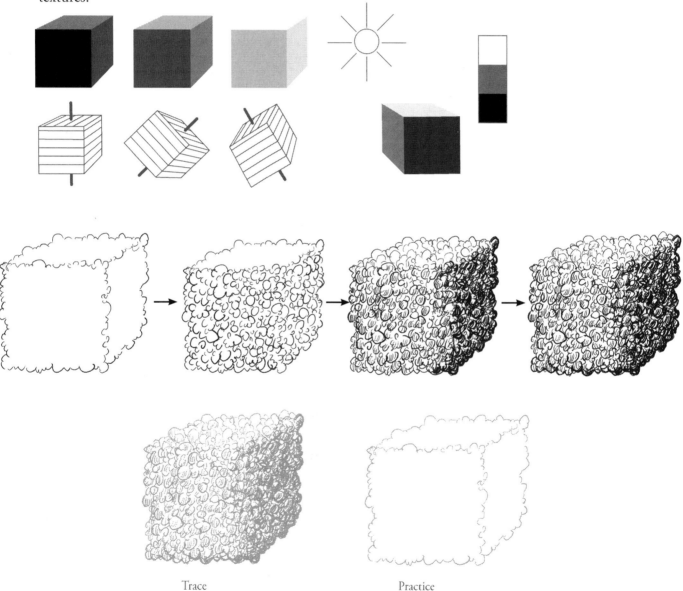

TEXTURE ON BLOCKS

Applying textures on block forms can easily be applied by following the 3-value system. First, determine the texture's pattern; then, study the form and identify its value pattern; finally, modify the texture to follow the form. Use block forms as a fun and easy way to practice creating life-like textures.

Trace

Practice

Practice

Practice

TEXTURE ON CYLINDERS

Applying textures on cylinders is an invaluable practice. You can easily think of many subjects with cylindrical forms like branches, animal limbs, tails, and other structures. Similar to shading curved surfaces, the key is to create a smooth transition between the light and shadow areas.

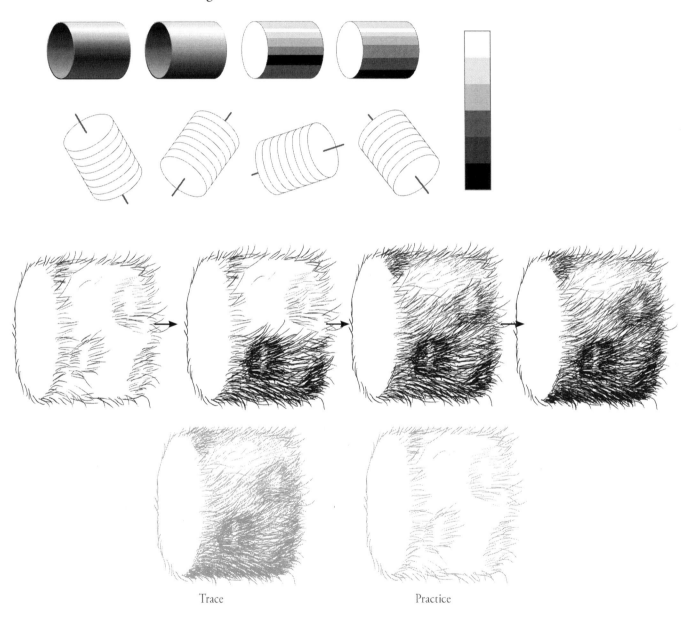

Trace

Practice

Practice

Practice

TEXTURE ON SPHERES

Remember with rendering spherical forms you either see the value gradation as diverging from or converging towards a point. Using this concept enables you to ensure that the texture is responding to light and shadow while following the form's curvature at the same time.

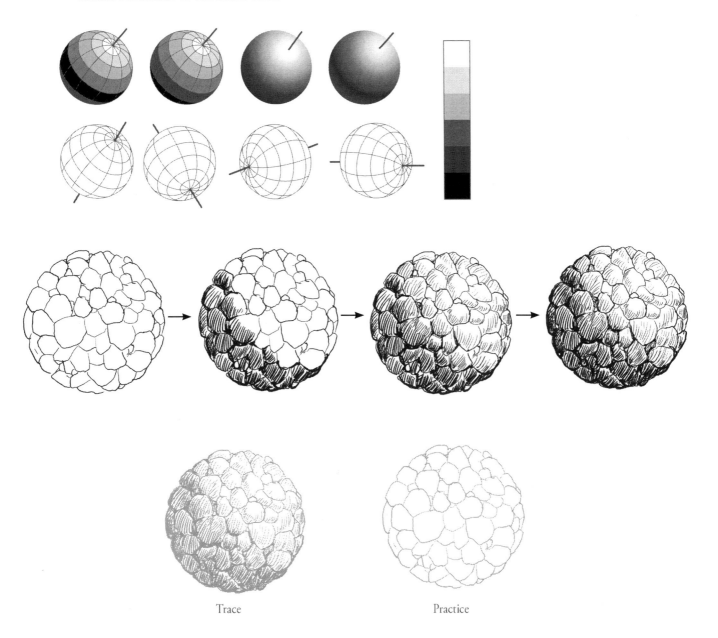

Trace

Practice

Practice   Practice

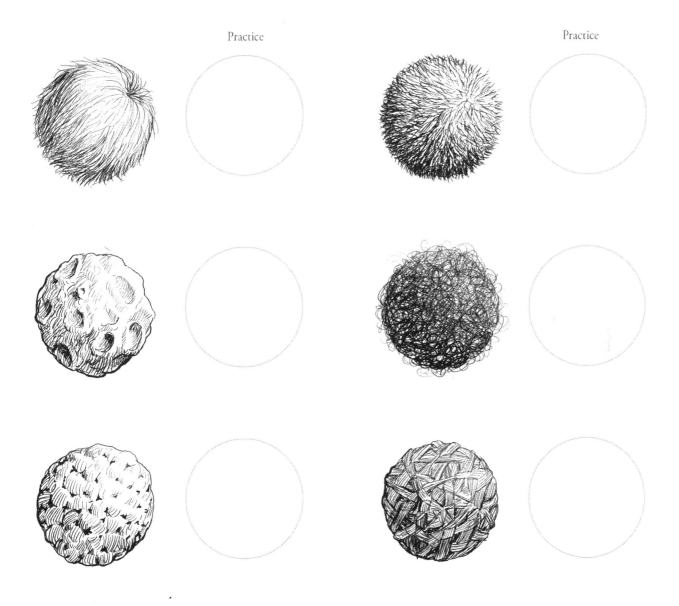

TEXTURE ON ORGANIC FORMS

The same principles apply here, but with a few modifications to account for the cross-contour of each form. Study the position and orientation of each form in relation to the light source to determine the value pattern.

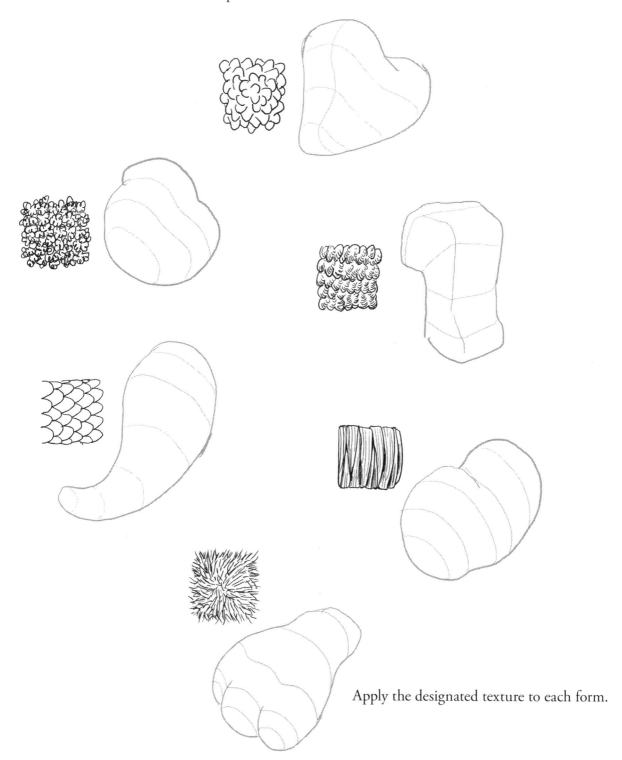

Apply the designated texture to each form.

PEN&INK
DRAWING
WORKBOOK

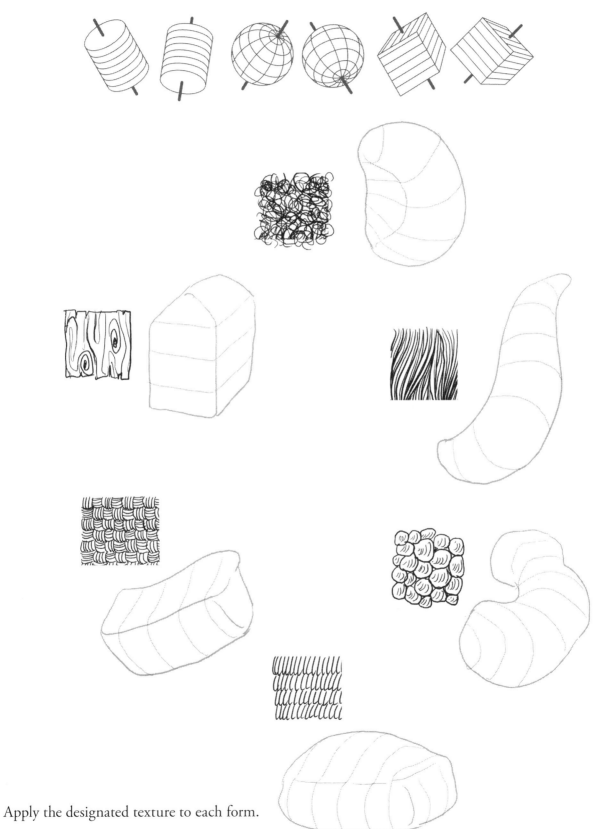

Apply the designated texture to each form.

4

Drawing Exercises

The follow drawing exercises are created for you to pull together the knowledge and skills you have acquired and apply them to a variety of subjects.

For each exercise, there is a visual breakdown showing the main stages of the process. Generally, the drawing starts with a light, broken outline. Next, a single layer of value is added. This sets the tone for the value pattern and distinguishes the main light and shadow areas. Then, more layers are added to deepen the values, if necessary. Blending is used to create a smooth transition between light and shadow areas. Finally, the drawing is refined. This often involves varying the weight of the outline, fine-tuning details, and touching up various areas as needed.

Over the course of these exercises, a wide range of concepts, skills, and techniques are utilized. Reflect on each one and think of ways to apply what you learn beyond this workbook.

GARLIC

This drawing is completed using only one type of stroke: curved hatching. Most of the five variations are used in order to convey mass, volume, light and shadow. Remember that by layering and reducing the spacing of strokes you can easily deepen the value. Do the opposite to convey areas of light.

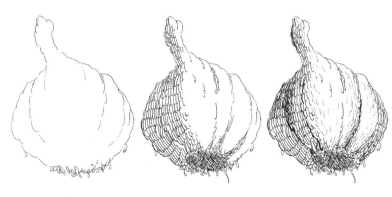

Trace

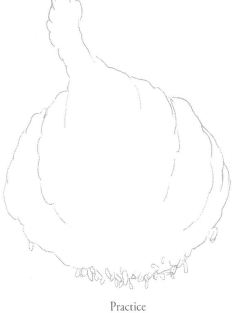

Practice

NOTES

SCRIBBLED EYE

Creating scribble drawings can be fun and liberating; however, they require a subtle balancing of tight and loose drawing. Make your scribbles a bit tighter and deeper when clarifying outlines and shapes, like when conveying the lower eyelid and iris. For conveying general value areas and mass, it is fine to let loose.

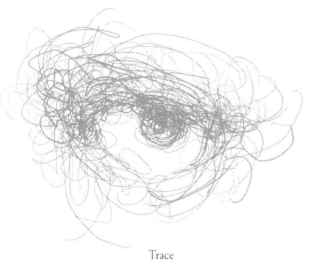

Trace

Practice

NOTES

HAT

Here is another example of a drawing using only one type of stroke. Layering the hatching creates the deep value in the shadow areas, and adjusting the spacing and size of the marks helps to convey the light value of the areas in light. The weight of the outline is varied to accentuate the effect of light and shadow.

NOTES

CALLA LILY

Flowing lines can be a challenge because of their length and undulating quality. The key is to draw them at a moderate pace and let the pen glide somewhat freely. Their flowing nature helps to capture the delicacy of the calla lily's petals.

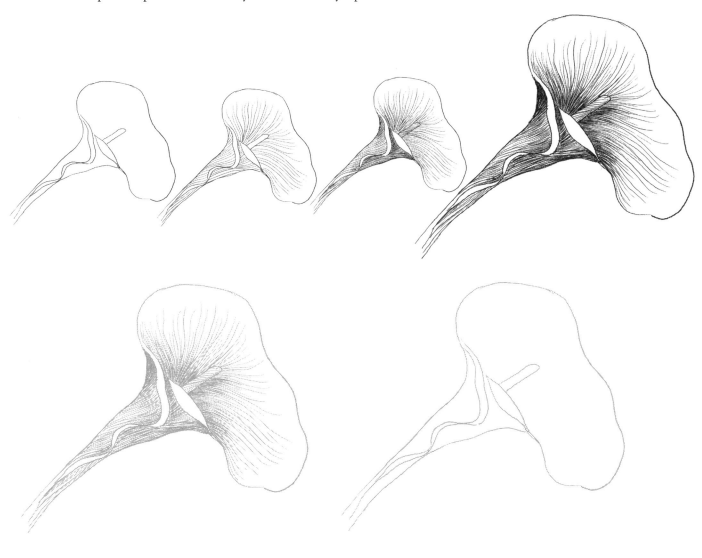

NOTES

BEETROOT

Leaves can be bit tricky to draw if you focus only on the little details. Squint your eyes to visualize the forms like wrinkles and folds of clothing. This makes it easier to understand the value pattern for placing your strokes. The beetroot's bulb is essentially a spherical form, and can be rendered as such.

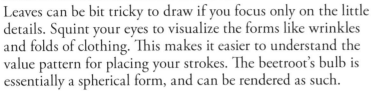

NOTES

MAKEUP BRUSH

This makeup brush enables you to combine a variety of the basic strokes. The handle has a wooden texture and hatching is used to render the effect of light and shadow. The bristles are drawn with uneven hatching and some layering is done to deepen the values.

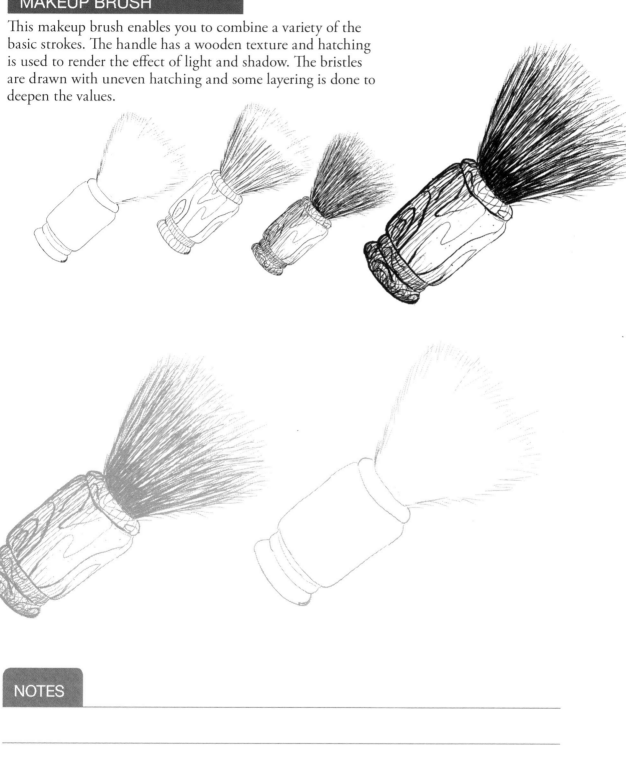

NOTES

STRIPPED BOW

This is a simple local value exercise. The deep-valued stripes follow the form of the bow and warp in and out of the folds and wrinkles. Note the difference in treatment of light and shadow between the stripes and the light area. This distinction is important to maintain.

NOTES

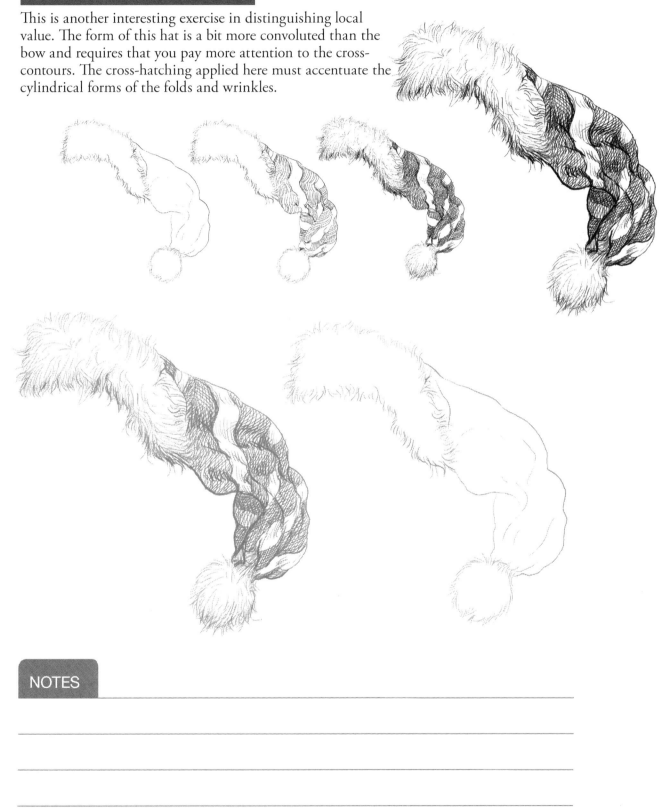

STRIPPED HAT

This is another interesting exercise in distinguishing local value. The form of this hat is a bit more convoluted than the bow and requires that you pay more attention to the cross-contours. The cross-hatching applied here must accentuate the cylindrical forms of the folds and wrinkles.

NOTES

_____

_____

_____

_____

HAMMER

The block form of this hammer makes it essentially a 3-value exercise. Note how the contours of the head and handle are defined by their textures. You can sense the hammer's worn quality more strongly because of its textured outline.

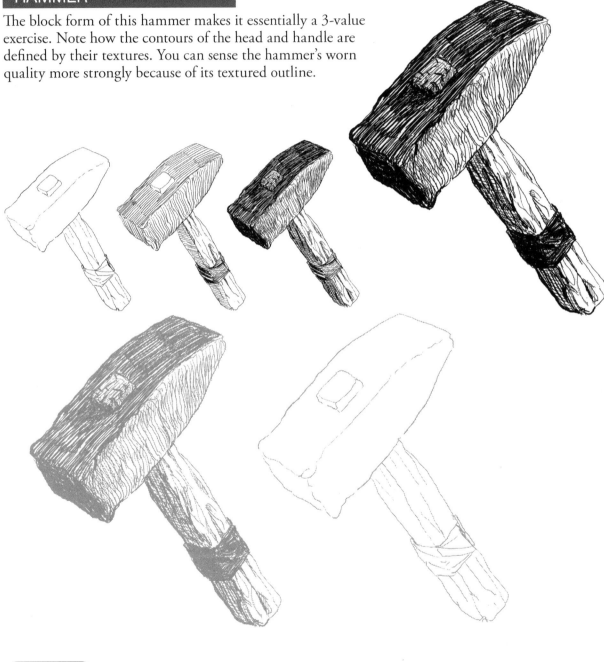

NOTES

MUSHROOM

This mushroom exemplifies the effective combination of stroke variations to convey texture, shading, and the distinction of local values. Notice the cylindrical form of the stalk and how the texture defines its contour while conveying the effects of light and shadow.

NOTES

PEN&INK DRAWING WORKBOOK

ORANGE

The texture created by the curved hatching fills this drawing of an orange with life. In this example, hatching is used to convey the light and shadow effects first before adding a layer of curved hatching to create the textural effect.

NOTES

LETTUCE

Hatching and flowing lines create the fabric-like feel of this lettuce's leaves. You can sense that the lettuce has a light local value based on the overall treatment. The value range is kept to a minimum, and even in areas of shadow the values barely reach a deep gray. This is a classic example of how to render light-colored subjects with pen and ink.

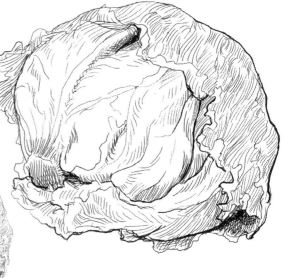

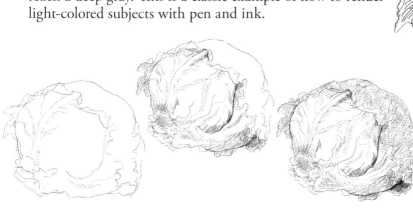

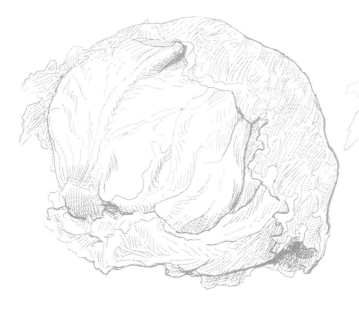

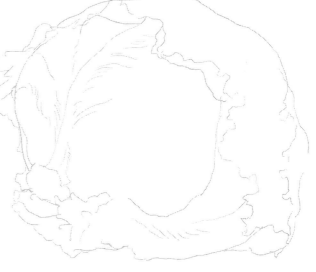

NOTES

SPOON

The general guidelines for conveying the effects of light and shadow are largely disregarded when drawing objects with metallic, reflective, or translucent surfaces. You have to rely largely on close observation. In general, capturing the textures of shiny metallic surfaces require the use of small, sharp, and abstract value-shapes. They sometimes appear to reveal semi-recognizable subject matter in their reflection.

NOTES

WOODEN PAIL

This is essentially a simple cylindrical form with a wood texture applied. First, try to separate the wood texture from the effects of light and shadow. Then, combine both as a unified whole so that each accentuates the other.

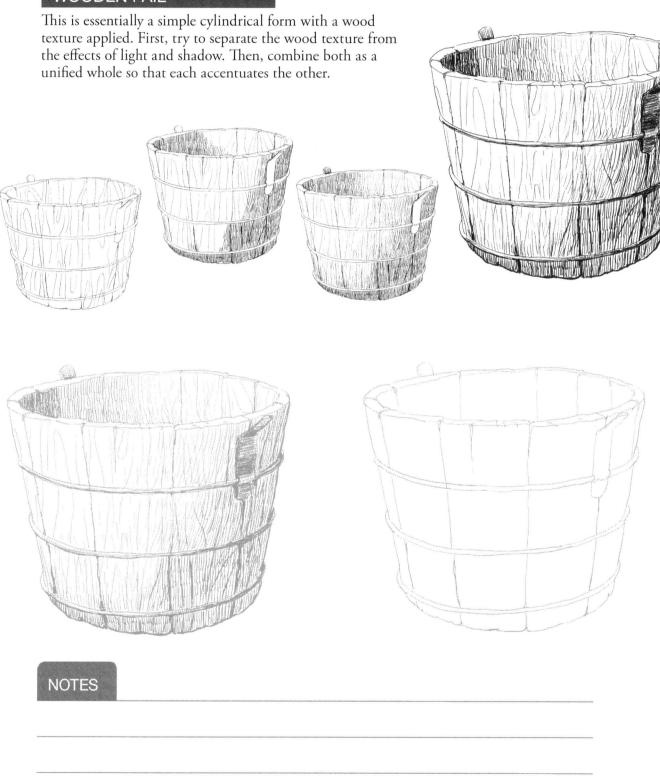

NOTES

_____

_____

_____

_____

DOG

The muzzle of this dog has a block-like form, and is rendered as such. You can see the texture on the ear is much more pronounced than on the top of its head or mouth area. This is revealed in the treatment of the contours. The stroke variations are in full effect when you compare the areas in shadow to the areas in light.

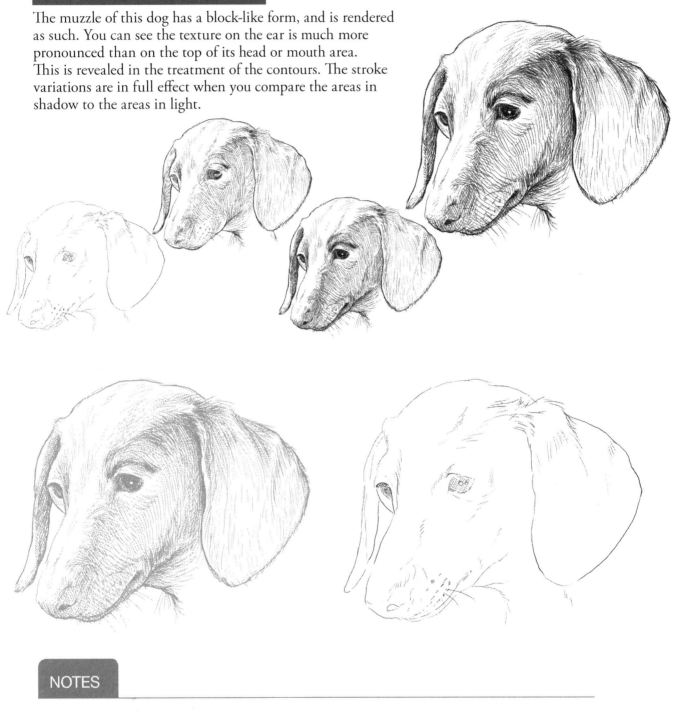

NOTES

RABBIT

This bunny presents a fun exercise in rendering texture and local value. In order to convey its light local value, care must be taken to not over-render its fur. This is done by generously spacing the strokes on the body. The texture is more strongly felt along the contours.

NOTES

TREE

A key to rendering trees is to visualize their leaves in clusters.
Don't make the mistake of trying to draw each individual
leaf. Simplify the overall form of its body and apply a pattern
that you believe best captures the texture of the leaves.

NOTES

LILY

Capturing the soft forms and delicate petals of flowers can be challenging. The strokes used here are mostly light and thin and follow the cross-contour of the petals. Cross-hatching is kept to a minimum and used in small shadow areas.

NOTES

BOULDER

Drawing rocks is good practice for learning how to render organic forms. Their rugged surfaces combined with their block-like forms create dynamic value patterns. Although there appears to be several sub-planes, the dominant underlying block form still enables you to essentially apply a 3-value approach.

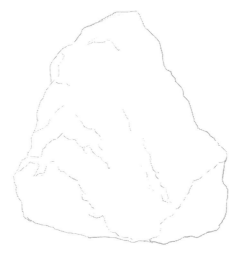

NOTES

GLASS JAR

Like with metallic surfaces, glass is effectively drawn based on close observation. Because of its translucent nature, much of the strokes used are short and broken. To help with creating the sense of transparency, think of the front details as layered over the interior and rear details. Make the lines of the front details more bold and pronounced, and make the strokes of background details light and thin.

NOTES

BRAID

Plan the placement of highlights when drawing dark hair. This will remind you to make the strokes light, thin, and more spaced where the highlights will be. In this drawing a white-ink pen is used to add more highlights. The loose strands of hair at the edges are added at the final stage to reinforce the texture and give the drawing more life.

NOTES

TOUCAN

This is another fun exercise in creating texture and distinguishing local values. In this drawing, the same types of strokes are used to render the light and dark feathers; however, in the deep-valued areas the strokes are more layered, tightly-packed, and heavier in weight. The strokes of the lighter feathers are sparse and thin.

NOTES

STIPPLED EYE

Stippling can be a consuming and tedious process, but it can also be deeply relaxing and therapeutic. You can see that this drawing starts with a dotted outline of the eye. This helps to keep the drawing clear and separates the different areas of value. To keep your stipples consistent, it is important to draw at a moderate pace.

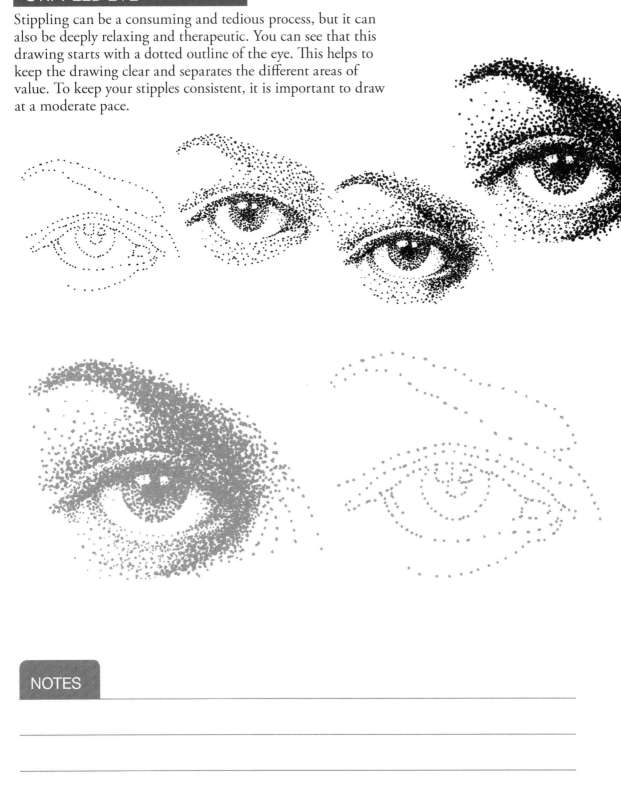

NOTES

NOSE

Drawing features of the head is generally challenging for many students. When rendering human forms with pen and ink, try to use strokes that follow the cross-contours and flow into adjacent forms. This creates a sense of continuity and oneness among the forms. No form of the face or head should be completely closed off.

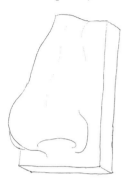
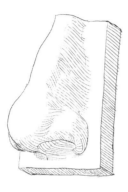
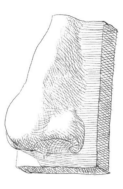
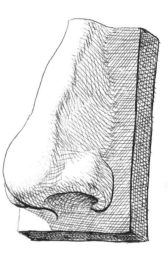

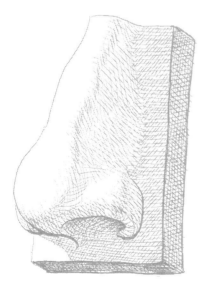
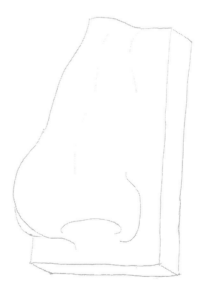

NOTES

FISH

When drawing scales try not to outline every single one. For scales in areas of light, break up their outlines and let the viewer's eye fill in the missing details. Failure to do this can cause the scales to look mechanical and artificial. The scales located at the light-shadow border have a strong visual impact because this is where the highest contrast in value occurs.

NOTES

BIRD

Feathers can sometimes be rendered using the same principle we apply to clusters of leaves on a tree. It isn't necessary to define every single feather. Instead, see clusters of feathers and render them as a whole. Save defining details for the larger and more conspicuous feathers of the wing, tail, or other areas. The dark wing feathers are treated like the dark feathers of the toucan in *Exercise 4.22*; the strokes are bold, tightly packed, and layered.

NOTES

CAT

Hatching strokes are used to depict this cat's hair. They are continuous and appear to follow undulating trails spreading away from the center of its face. Sometimes it helps to pencil in the growth patterns of animal fur and hair like this, so your ink strokes maintain order and stay on their path.

NOTES

WORK BOOT

This demonstrates how easy it is to find subjects for practice. Look around the your house, desk, or outside and you will find countless simple but visually engaging items that would make great subjects for drawing. Remember this: it isn't what you look at that matters, it is what you see.

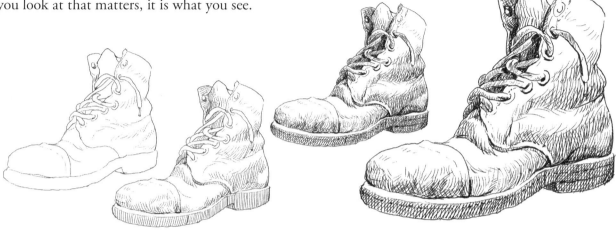

NOTES

HOUSE

This little house is essentially a simple block form with texture and details applied. The texture on the side of the house in light is loosely drawn. They are not meticulously defined, which would give the surface a mechanical and artificial feel. Further, the textures in shadow are left a bit obscure due to the lack of light. For the roof, it may help to pencil in some construction lines to guide the placement of the shingles.

NOTES

BURGER

This burger displays an interesting array of strokes, textures, values, and interesting details. There is minimal rendering on the bun and cheese due to their light local value. Stipples, hatching, and a little cross-hatching account for all the strokes used throughout the drawing. Small, round pebble-like shapes create the texture of the meat and tightly-spaced hatching conveys the value of the tomato slices. Closely study the drawing and you will realize it is not as intimidating as it appears.

NOTES

Index

Made in the USA
Columbia, SC
31 October 2018